NICOTEXT

Cult Movie Quote Book

It is the authors' sincere wish that this book will lead to an increased interest in film. We would also like to express our deepest gratitude towards film companies, screenplaywriters and casts. Without them this book would not excist.

If you find any wrongly quoted movies, or other mistakes PLEASE contact us and we will correct it in the next edition.

Respectfully, NICOTEXT

Fredrik Colting
Carl-Johan Gadd
Stefan Sjölander
Edited by: Lara Allen

©2005 NICOTEXT
info@nicotext.com

Printed in Canada

ISBN 91-974396-3-0

www.nicotext.com

"I must be crazy to be in a loony bin like this."

ONE FLEW OVER THE CUCKOO'S NEST

Play the movie quiz game!

Rules:
There are six movie quotes on each right page.
The answerss are on the following left page.
Use a dice and guess which movie the quotes are from.
Read one page each and pass the book on.
Note points on a piece of paper.
Play alone or with your friends!

1. -I haven't got a brain... only straw.
    -How can you talk if you haven't got a brain?
    -I don't know. But some people without brains
    do an awful lot of talking, don't they?
    -Yes, I guess you're right.

    Wizard of Oz

2. -It had been a wonderful evening and what I needed now,
    to give it the perfect ending, was a little of the Ludwig Von.

3. -We're gonna need a bigger boat.

    Jaws

4. -It's got a cop motor, a 440 cubic inch plant, it's got cop tires,
    cop suspensions, cop shocks. It's a model made before catalytic
    converters so it'll run good on regular gas. What do you say,
    is it the new Bluesmobile or what?
    -Fix the cigarette lighter.

5. -When a man is chasing a woman through an alley with
    a butcher's knife and a hard-on, I figure he isn't out collecting
    for the Red Cross!

6. -I don't give a good fuck what you know or don't know.
    I'm going to torture you anyway.

ANSWERS >

1. **THE WIZARD OF OZ**
   1939, USA
   Director: Victor Fleming
   Cast: Judy Garland, Ray Bolger, Bert Lahr
   Screenplay: Noel Langley, Florence Ryerson and Edgar Allan Woolf
   Based on the book by L. Frank Baum

2. **A CLOCKWORK ORANGE**
   1971, USA
   Director: Stanley Kubrick
   Cast: Malcolm McDowell, Patrick Magee, Adrienne Corri
   Screenplay: Stanley Kubrick
   Based on the book by Anthony Burgess

3. **JAWS**
   1975, USA
   Director: Steven Spielberg
   Cast: Roy Scheider, Robert Shaw, Richard Dreyfuss
   Screenplay: Peter Benchley, Carl Gottlieb, John Milius,
   Howard Sackler and Robert Shaw
   Based on the book by Peter Benchley

4. **THE BLUES BROTHERS**
   1980, USA
   Director: John Landis
   Cast: John Belushi, Dan Aykroyd, Cap Calloway
   Screenplay: Dan Aykroyd and John Landis

5. **DIRTY HARRY**
   1971, USA
   Director: Don Siegal
   Cast: Clint Eastwood, Harry Guardino, Reni Santoni
   Screenplay: Harry Julian Fink, Rita M. Fink, Dean Riesner
   and John Milius

6. **RESERVOIR DOGS**
   1992, USA
   Director: Quentin Tarantino
   Cast: Harvey Keitel, Tim Roth, Michael Madsen
   Screenplay: Roger Avary and Quentin Tarantino

1. -You call yourself a free spirit, a wild thing, and you're terrified somebody's gonna stick you in a cage. Well, baby, you're already in that cage. You built it yourself. And it's not bounded in the west by Tulip, Texas, or in the east by Somali-land. It's wherever you go. Because no matter where you run, you just end up running into yourself.

2. -When people think you're dying, they really, really listen to you, instead of just...
    -instead of just waiting for their turn to speak?

3. -They'll talk to ya and talk to ya and talk to ya about individual freedom. But they see a free individual, it's gonna scare 'em.

4. -I can remember when I was a little boy. My grandmother and I could hold conversations entirely without ever opening our mouths.

5. -If I have any more fun today I don't think I can take it!

6. -We got a secret weapon. God is our co-pilot!
    -God is our co-pilot? Remember our car?
    -Yeah?
    -Two seats!
    -Two seats...?
    -Where's he gonna sit? Where?

9

ANSWERS >

1. BREAKFAST AT TIFFANY'S
    1961, USA
    Director: Blake Edwards
    Cast: Audrey Hepburn, George Peppard
    Screenplay: Truman Capote, George Axelrod

2. FIGHT CLUB
    1999, USA
    Director: David Fincher
    Cast: Brad Pitt, Edward Norton, Helena Bonham Carter
    Screenplay: Jim Uhls
    Based on the book by Chuck Palahniuk

3. EASY RIDER
    1969, USA
    Director: Dennis Hopper
    Cast: Peter Fonda, Dennis Hopper, Jack Nicholson.
    Screenplay: Peter Fonda, Dennis Hopper and Terry Southern

4. THE SHINING
    1980, USA
    Director: Stanley Kubrick
    Cast: Jack Nicholson, Shelley Duvall, Danny Lloyd
    Screenplay: Stanley Kubrick and Diane Johnson
    Based on the book by Stephen King

5. THE TEXAS CHAINSAW MASSACRE
    1974, USA
    Director: Tobe Hopper
    Cast: Marilyn Burns, Gunner Hansen, Ed Neal
    Screenplay: Kim Henkel and Tobe Hooper

6. THE CANNONBALL RUN
    1981, USA
    Director: Hal Needham
    Cast: Burt Reynolds, Roger Moore, Farrah Fawcett
    Screenplay: Brock Yates

1. -I can't make out whether you're a
    bloody madman or just half-witted.
    -I have the same problem, sir.

2. -Is there someone inside you?
    -Sometimes.
    -Who is it?
    -I don't know.
    -Is it Captain Howdy?
    -I don't know.
    -If I ask him to tell me, will you let him answers?
    -No!
    -Why not?
    -I'm afraid.

3. -How do you explain school to a higher intelligence?

4. -This snakeskin jacket symbolizes my individuality
    and belief in personal freedom.

5. -Look at your algebra book. It looks like it's never
    even been opened!
    -I only use it on special equations

6. -More human than human is our motto.

1.   LAWRENCE OF ARABIA
      1962, UNITED KINGDOM
      Director: David Lean
      Cast: Peter O'Toole, Alec Guinness, Anthony Quinn
      Screenplay: T.E. Lawrence, Robert Bolt and Michael Wilson

2.   EXORCIST, THE
      1973, USA
      Director: William Friedkin
      Cast: Ellen Burstyn, Max Von Sydow, Linda Blair
      Screenplay: William Peter Blatty

3.   E.T THE EXTRA-TERRESTRIAL
      1982, USA
      Director: Steven Spielberg
      Cast: Dee Wallace, Henry Thomas, Peter Coyote
      Screenplay: Melissa Mathison

4.   WILD AT HEART
      1990, USA
      Director: David Lynch
      Cast: Nicolas Cage, Laura Dern, Diane Ladd
      Screenplay: David Lynch
      Based on the book by Barry Gifford

5.   ROCK 'N' ROLL HIGH SCHOOL
      1979, USA
      Director: Allan Arkush, Joe Dante
      Cast: P.J Soles, Vincent van Patten, Clint Howard
      Screenplay: Richard Whitley, Russ Dronch

6.   BLADE RUNNER
      1982, USA
      Director: Ridley Scott
      Cast: Harrison Ford, Rutger Hauer, Sean Young
      Screenplay: Hampton Fancher, David Webb Peoples, Roland Kibbel
      Based on the book by Philip K. Dick

1. -John Connor gave me a picture of you once. I didn't know why at the time. It was very old, torn-faded. You were young like you are now. You seemed just a little sad. I used to always wonder what you were thinking at that moment. I memorized every line, every curve. I came across time for you, Sarah, I love you, I always have.

   Terminator

2. -I think someone should just take this city and just... just flush it down the fuckin' toilet.

   Taxi Driver

3. -I don't think about that much with one shot anymore, Mike.
   -You have to think about one shot. One shot is what it's all about. A deer's gotta be taken with one shot.

4. -1,000 British soldiers have been massacred. While I stood here talking peace, a war has started.

5. -I am not an animal! I am a human being! I am a man!

6. -Cherry was right. You're soft, you should have let 'em kill me, 'cause I'm gonna kill you. I'll catch up with ya. I don't know when, but I'll catch up. Every time you turn around, expect to see me, 'cause one time you'll turn around and I'll be there. I'm gonna kill ya, Matt.

ANSWERS >

1.   THE TERMINATOR
      1984, USA
      Director: James Cameron
      Cast: Arnold Schwartzenegger, Michael Biehn,
      Linda Hamilton
      Screenplay: James Cameron, Gale Anne Hurd,
      William Wisher Jr and Harlan Ellison

2.   TAXI DRIVER
      1976, USA
      Director: Martin Scorsese
      Cast: Robert De Niro, Cybill Shepherd, Harvey Keitel
      Screenplay: Paul Schrader

3.   THE DEER HUNTER
      1978, USA
      Director: Michael Cimino
      Cast: Robert De Niro, Christopher Walken, Meryl Streep
      Screenplay: Michael Cimino, Louis Garfinkle, Quinn K. Redeker and
      Deric Washburn

4.   ZULU
      1963, UNITED KINGDOM
      Director: Cy Endfield
      Cast: Stanley Baker, Jack Hawkins, Ulla Jacobsson
      Screenplay: John Prebble, John Prebble and Cy Endfield

5.   THE ELEPHANT MAN
      1980, USA
      Director: David Lynch
      Cast: Anthony Hopkins, John Hurt, Anne Bancroft
      Screenplay: Christopher De Vore, Eric Bergren and David Lynch
      Based on the book by Sir Frederick Treves and Ashley Montagu

6.   RED RIVER
      1948, USA
      Director: Howard Hawks
      Cast: John Wayne, Montgomery Clift, Walter Brennan
      Screenplay: Borden Chase, Borden Chase and Charles Schnee

1. -You're not the boss of me, Jack! You're not the king of Dirk! I'm
    the boss of me! I'm the king of me. I'm Dirk Diggler! I'm the star!
    It's my big dick and I say when we roll!

2. -How do you feel?
    -Fast and loose.
    -In the gut, I mean.
    -Tight, but good.

3. -Faster than a speeding bullet! More powerful than a locomotive!
    Able to leap tall buildings with a single bound, the infant of
    Krypton is now the Man of Steel.

    Superman

4. -I just wanna know how one becomes a janitor because Andrew
    here is very interested in pursuing a career in the custodial arts.

5. -I can't figure out if you're a detective or a pervert.
    -Well, that's for me to know and you to find out.

6. -I don't think it's nice, you laughin'. You see, my mule don't like
    people laughing. He gets the crazy idea you're laughin' at him.
    Now if you apologize, like I know you're going to, I might convince
    him that you really didn't mean it.

1. **BOOGIE NIGHTS**
    1997, USA
    Director: Paul Thomas Anderson
    Cast: Mark Wahlberg, Burt Reynolds, Julianne Moore
    Screenplay: Paul Thomas Anderson

2. **THE HUSTLER**
    1961, USA
    Director: Robert Rossen
    Cast: Paul Newman, Jackie Gleason, Piper Lauire
    Screenplay: Sidney Carroll and Robert Rossen
    Based on the book by Walter Tevis

3. **SUPERMAN**
    1941, USA
    Director: Dave Fleischer
    Cast: Bud Collyer (voice), Joan Alexander (voice)
    Screenplay: Seymour Kneitel, Joe Shuster

4. **THE BREAKFAST CLUB**
    1985, USA
    Director: John Hughes
    Cast: Emilio Esteves, Judd Nelson, Molly Ringwald
    Screenplay: John Hughes

5. **BLUE VELVET**
    1986, USA
    Director: David Lynch
    Cast: Kyle MacLachlan, Isabella Rossellini, Dennis Hopper
    Screenplay: David Lynch

6. **A FISTFULL OF DOLLARS**
    1964, ITALY
    Director: Sergio Leone
    Cast: Clint Eastwood, Marianne Kand, Giana Maria Volonté
    Screenplay: A. Bonzzoni, Victor Andrés Catena

1. -The 1961 Ferrari 250GT California. Less than a hundred were
   made. My father spent three years restoring this car.
   It is his love, it is his passion.
   -It is his fault he didn't lock the garage.

2. -A man can convince anyone he's somebody else,
   but never himself.

3. -Good morning! And in case I don't see you: good afternoon,
   good evening and good night!

4. -Now, I don't have to tell you good folks what's been happening
   in our beloved little town. Sheriff murdered, crops burned, stores
   looted, people stampeded, and cattle raped. The time has come
   to act, and act fast. I'm leaving.

   Blazing Saddles

5. -If I was an imitation, a perfect imitation, how would you
   know it was me?

6. -I went to the woods because I wanted to live deliberately,
   I wanted to live deep and suck out all the marrow of life.
   To put to rest all that was not life, and not, when I had come
   to die, discover that I had not lived.

   Dead Poet's Society

17

ANSWERS >

1.   FERRIS BUELLER'S DAY OFF
      1986, USA
      Director: John Hughes
      Cast: Matthew Broderick, Alan Ruck, Mia Sara
      Screenplay: John Hughes

2.   THE USUAL SUSPECTS
      1995, USA
      Director: Bryan Singer
      Cast: Stephen Baldwin, Gabriel Byrne, Chazz Palminteri
      Screenplay: Christopher McQuarrie

3.   THE TRUMAN SHOW
      1998, USA
      Director: Peter Weir
      Cast: Jim Carrey, Laura Linney, Ed Harris
      Screenplay: Andrew Niccol

4.   BLAZING SADDLES
      1973, USA
      Director: Mel Brooks
      Cast: Cleavon Little, Gene Wilder, Harvey Korman
      Screenplay: Andrew Bergman, Mel Brooks, Richard Pryor,
      Norman Steinberg and Alan Uger

5.   THE THING
      1982, USA
      Director: John Carpenter
      Cast: Kurt Russell, Richard Dysart, A Wilford Brimley
      Screenplay: John W. Campbell Jr and Bill Lancaster

6.   DEAD POETS SOCIETY
      1989, USA
      Director: Peter Weir
      Cast: Robin Williams, Robert Sean Leonard, Ethan Hawke
      Screenplay: Tom Schulman

1. -Housework is like bad sex. Every time I do it I swear I will
    never do it again. Until the next time company comes.

2. -How did you find America?
    -Turned left at Greenland.

3. -Don't you think it would be better if you referred to
    it as him?
    -If you say so.
    -Your compassion's overwhelming, doctor.

4. -And now, ladies and gentlemen, before I tell you any more,
    I'm going to show you the greatest thing your eyes have ever
    beheld. He was a king and a god in the world he knew, but
    now he comes to civilization merely a captive - a show to
    gratify your curioslty.

    king kong

5. -This is paradise, I'm tellin' ya. This town is like a great
    big pussy jus' waitin' to get fucked.

6. -I get it. No questions.
    -No questions, no lies.
    -No questions, no truth, either.

ANSWERS >

1.   CAN'T STOP THE MUSIC
      1980, USA
      Director: Nancy Walker
      Cast: Alex Briley, David Hodo, Glenn Hughes
      Screenplay: Alan Carr, Bronte Woodard

2.   A HARD DAY'S NIGHT
      1964, UNITED KINGDOM
      Director: Richard Lester
      Cast: John Lennon, Paul McCartney, George Harrison
      Screenplay: Alun Owen

3.   HALLOWEEN
      1978, USA
      Director: John Carpenter
      Cast: Donald Pleasence, Jamie Lee Curtis, Nancy Loomis
      Screenplay: John Carpenter and Debra Hill

4.   KING KONG
      1976, USA
      Director: John Guillermin
      Cast: Jeff Bridges, Charles Grodin, Jessica Lange
      Screenplay: Merian C. Cooper, Edgar Wallace, James Ashmore
      Creelman, Ruth Rose and Lorenzo Semple Jr.

5.   SCARFACE
      1983, USA
      Director: Brian De Palma
      Cast: Al Pacino, Steven Bauer, Michelle Pfeiffer
      Screenplay: Oliver Stone and Howard Hawks
      Based on the book by Armitage Trail

6.   XANADU
      1980, USA
      Director: Robert Greenwald
      Cast: Olivia Newton John, Gene Kelly, Michael Beck
      Screenplay: Richard Christian Danus and Marc Reid Rubel

1. -I see men - sixty, seventy years old - breaking their balls to stay fit! What for? When I die, I want to be sick, not healthy.

2. -Looking at the cake is like looking at the future: until you've tasted it what do you really know? And then, of course, it's too late.

3. -So, how long you've been in Mexico?
    -A week. I mean a day.
    -Well, which is it? A week or a day?
    -A weekday.

4. Choose a future. Choose life... But why would I want to do a thing like that? I chose not to choose life, I choose something else. And the reasons? There are no reasons. Who needs reasons when you've got heroin?

5. -There are two kinds of people in this world;
    Those with loaded guns, and those who dig. You dig.

6. Remember those posters that said, Today is the first day of the rest of your life? Well, that's true of every day but one... The day you die.

 ANSWERS >

1.	**THE WITCHES OF EASTWICK**
	1987, USA
	Director: George Miller
	Cast: Jack Nicholson, Cher, Susan Sarandon
	Screenplay: Michael Cristofer. Based on the book by John Updike

2.	**EXCALIBUR**
	1981, UNITED KINGDOM
	Director: John Boorman
	Cast: Nicol Williamson, Nigel Terry, Helen Mirren
	Screenplay: Rospo Pallenberg and John Boorman
	Based on the book by Thomas Malory

3.	**UP IN SMOKE**
	1978, USA
	Director: Lou Adler
	Cast: Cheech Marin, Tommy Chong, Stacy Keach
	Screenplay: Tommy Chong and Cheech Marin

4.	**TRAINSPOTTING**
	1996, UNITED KINGDOM
	Director: Danny Boyle
	Cast: Ewan McGregor, Ewan Bremmer, Jonny Lee Miller
	Screenplay: John Hodge. Based on the book by Irvine Welsh

5.	**THE GOOD, THE BAD, AND THE UGLY**
	1966, ITALY/SPAIN
	Director: Sergio Leone
	Cast: Clint Eastwood, Lee Van Cleef, Eli Wallach
	Screenplay: Luciano Vincenzoni, Sergio Leone, Agenore Incrocci and
	Furio Scarpelli

6.	**AMERICAN BEAUTY**
	1999, USA
	Director: Sam Mendes
	Cast: Kevin Spacey, Annette Bening, Thora Birch
	Screenplay: Alan Ball

1. -I have existed from the morning of the world and I shall exist until the last star falls from the night. Although I have taken the form of Gaius Caligula, I am all men, as I am no man, and therefore I am a God.

2. -I realized my true calling in life.
   -What's that?
   -Shit, man, I'm a natural born killer.

3. -I'm not gonna debate you, Jerry.
   -Okay.
   -I'm not gonna sit here and debate.

4. -I'm not the Messiah! Will you please listen? I am not the Messiah! Do you understand?! Honestly!
   -Only the true Messiah denies His divinity.
   -What?! Well, what sort of chance does that give me? All right! I am the Messiah!
   -He is! He is the Messiah!
   -Now, fuck off!
   -How shall we fuck off, O Lord?   Monty Python's Life of Brian

5. -Secret's in the sauce.

6. -I run a couple of newspapers. What do you do?
   Citizen Kane

23   ANSWERS >

1. **CALIGULA**
   1980, ITALY/USA
   Director: Tinto Brass
   Cast: Malcolm McDowell, Peter O'Toole, Teresa Ann Savoy
   Screenplay: Gore Vidal, Bob Guccione, Giancarlo Lui, Masolino D'Amico, Franco Rossellini and Roberto Rossellini

2. **NATURAL BORN KILLERS**
   1994, USA
   Director: Oliver Stone
   Cast: Woody Harrelson, Juliette Lewis, Robert Downey Jr
   Screenplay: Quentin Tarantino, David Veloz, Richard Rutowski and Oliver Stone

3. **FARGO**
   1996, USA
   Director: Joel Coen
   Cast: Frances McDormand, William H Macy, Steve Buscemi
   Screenplay: Joel Coen and Ethan Coen

4. **MONTY PYTHON'S LIFE OF BRIAN**
   1979, UNITED KINGDOM
   Director: Terry Jones
   Cast: Graham Chapman, John Cleese, Terry Gilliam
   Screenplay: Graham Chapman, John Cleese, Terry Gilliam, Eric Idle, Terry Jones and Michael Palin

5. **FRIED GREEN TOMATOES**
   1991, USA
   Director: Jon Avnet
   Cast: Kathy Bates, Jessica Tandy, Mary Stuart Masterson
   Screenplay: Carol Sobieski, Fannie Flagg
   Based on the book by Fannie Flagg

6. **CITIZEN KANE**
   1941, USA
   Director: Orson Welles
   Cast: Orson Welles, Joseph Cotten, Everett Sloane
   Screenplay: Herman J. Mankiewicz, Orson Welles and John Houseman

1. -We can't go around measuring our goodness by what we
    don't do, by what we deny ourselves, by what we resist and
    who we exclude. I think we got to measure goodness by what
    we embrace, by what we create, and who we include.

    Chocolat

2. This here's Miss Bonnie Parker. I'm Clyde Barrow.
    We rob banks.

    Bonnie and Clyde

3. -Chief, if I were surrounded by, say six, or eight of these things,
    would I stand a chance?
    -Well, if you had a gun, shoot 'em in the head. If you didn't,
    get a torch and burn 'em, they go up pretty easy. Beat 'em
    or burn 'em.

4. -Uh-uh, Mother-m-mother, uh, what is the phrase?
    She isn't quite herself today.

5. -The only evidence I see of the antichrist here,
    is everyone's desire to see him at work.

6. -Before he came down here, it never snowed. And afterwards,
    it did. I don't think it would be snowing now if he weren't still up
    there. Sometimes you can still catch me dancing in it.

    Edward Scissorhands

ANSWERS >

1. CHOCOLAT
   2000, USA
   Director: Lasse Hallström
   Cast: Johnny Depp, Alfred Molina, Lena Olin,
   Juliette Binoche
   Screenplay: Robert Nelson Jacobs

2. BONNIE AND CLYDE
   1967, USA
   Director: Arthur Penn
   Cast: Warren Beatty, Faye Dunaway, Michael J Pollard
   Screenplay: David Newman, Robert Benton and Robert Towne

3. NIGHT OF THE LIVING DEAD
   1968, USA
   Director: George A Romero
   Cast: Duane Jones, Judith O'Dea, Russell Streiner
   Screenplay: George A. Romero and John A. Russo

4. PSYCHO
   1960, USA
   Director: Alfred Hitchcook
   Cast: Anthony Perkins, Janet Leigh, Vera Miles
   Screenplay: Joseph Stefano. Based on the book by Robert Bland

5. THE NAME OF THE ROSE
   1986, FRANCE/ITALY/WESTGERMANY
   Director: Jean Jacques Annaud
   Cast: Sean Connery, F. Murray Abraham, Christian Slater
   Screenplay: Andrew Birkin, Gérard Brach, Howard Franklin and
   Alain Godard
   Based on the book by Umberto Eco

6. EDWARD SCISSORHANDS
   1990, USA
   Director: Tim Burton
   Cast: Johnny Depp, Winona Ryder, Dianne Wiest
   Screenplay: Tim Burton and Caroline Thompson

1. -Let me put it this way, Mr. Amer. The 9000 series is the most
    reliable computer ever made. No 9000 computer has ever made
    a mistake or distorted information. We are all, by any practical
    definition of the words, foolproof and incapable of error.

    2001

2. -It's not easy being a cast-iron bitch. It takes discipline,
    years of training... A lot of people don't appreciate that.

3. -My style, you can call the art of fighting without fighting.

4. -Nothing's riding on this except the - uh - first amendment to the
    Constitution, freedom of the press, and maybe the future of the
    country. Not that any of that matters, but if you guys fuck up
    again, I'm going to get mad. Goodnight.

5. -The Irish are the blacks of Europe. Dubliners are the blacks
    of Ireland. North Dubliners are the blacks of Dublin.

6. - If you were mine, I wouldn't share you with anybody or
    anything. It'd be just you and me. We'd be the center of it all.
    I know it would feel a lot more like love than being left alone
    with your work.

1.   2001: A SPACE ODYSSEY
        1968, UNITED KINGDOM
        Director: Stanley Kubrick
        Cast: Keir Dullea, William Sylvester, Gary Lockwood
        Screenplay: Stanley Kubrick and Arthur C. Clarke

2.   THE ABYSS
        1989, USA
        Director: James Cameron
        Cast: Ed Harris, Mary Elizabeth Mastrantonio, Michael Biehn
        Screenplay: James Cameron

3.   ENTER THE DRAGON
        1973, USA
        Director: Robert Clouse
        Cast: Bruce Lee, John Saxon, Jim Kelly
        Screenplay: Michael Allin

4.   ALL THE PRESIDENTS MEN
        1976, USA
        Director: Alan J Pakula
        Cast: Robert Redford, Dustin Hoffman, Jason Roberts
        Screenplay: William Goldman
        Based on the book by Carl Bernstein and Bob Woodward

5.   THE COMMITMENTS
        1991, UNITED KINGDOM
        Director: Alan Parker
        Cast: Robert Arkins, Michael Aherne, Angeline Ball
        Screenplay: Dick Clement, Ian La Frenais and Roddy Doyle
        Based on the book by Roddy Doyle

6.   REDS
        1981, USA
        Director: Warren Beatty
        Cast: Warren Beatty, Diane Keaton, Edward Herrmann
        Screenplay: Warren Beatty, Trevor Griffiths, Elaine May, John Reed,
        Jeremy Pikser and Peter S. Feibleman

1. -I just wish for once that you could be in my shoes, Mr. Prosecutor, and then you would know something that you don't know, mercy: That the concept of a society is based on the quality of that mercy; its sense of fair play; its sense of justice! But I guess that's like asking a bear to shit in the toilet.

2. -Afraid this tea is pathetic. I must have used those wretched leaves about twenty times. It's not that I mind so much. Tea without milk is so uncivilized.

3. -Your reality, sir, is lies and balderdash and I'm delighted to say that I have no grasp of it whatsoever.

4. -The wind whispers of fear and hate. The war has killed love. And those that confess to the Angka are punished, and no one dare ask where they go. Here, only the silent survive.

5. -If you want me to stop, tell me now.
   -No one's asking you to.

6. -I've just been to the dedication of the new children's park.
   -Yeah. How did that go?
   -Janice Van Meter got hit with a baseball. It was fabulous.
   -Was she hurt?
   -I doubt it. She got hit in the head.

ANSWERS >

1. **MIDNIGHT EXPRESS**
   1978, UNITED KINGDOM
   Director: Alan Parker
   Cast: Brad Davis, Irene Miracle, Bo Hopkins
   Screenplay: Oliver Stone
   Based on the book by Billy Hayes and William Hoffer

2. **THE GREAT ESCAPE**
   1962, USA
   Director: John Sturges,
   Cast: Steve McQueen, James Garner, Richard Attenborough
   Screenplay: James Clavell and W.R. Burnett
   Based on the book by Paul Brickhill

3. **THE ADVENTURES OF BARON MUNCHAUSEN**
   1989, UNITED KINGDOM
   Director: Terry Gilliam
   Cast: John Neville, Eric Idle, Sarah Polley
   Screenplay: Terry Gilliam and Charles McKeown
   Based on the book by Rudolph Erich Raspe

4. **THE KILLING FIELDS**
   1984, UNITED KINGDOM
   Director: Roland Joffe
   Cast: Sam Waterston, Haing S Ngor, John Malkovich
   Screenplay: Bruce Robinson

5. **THE BRIDGES OF MADISON COUNTY**
   1995, USA
   Director: Clint Eastwood
   Cast: Clint Eastwood, Meryl Streep, Annie Corley
   Screenplay: Richard LaGravenese
   Based on the book by Robert James Waller.

6. **STEEL MAGNOLIAS**
   1989, USA
   Director: Herbert Ross
   Cast: Sally Field, Dolly Parton, Julia Roberts
   Screenplay: Robert Harling

1. -But Mama, the men she finds. The last one was so
   old and he was bald. He had no hair.
   -A poor girl without a dowry can't be so paticular.
   You want hair, marry a monkey.

2. -You know something? You read too many comic books.

3. -This young man has had a very trying rookie season,
   with the litigation, the notoriety, his subsequent deportation
   to Canada and that country's refusal to accept him.
   Number six, Ogie Oglethorpe.

4. -There are two ways to disable an alligator, Mr. Bond.
   -I don't suppose you'd tell me what they are.
   -One way is to jab a pen right above it's eye.
   -And the other way?
   -Oh, the other way is twice as simple. Just stick your hand in it's
   mouth and pull out all it's teeth. Heh, heh.

5. -Well, does he make you laugh?
   -He doesnt make me cry.

   Ocean's Eleven

6. -Well I wouldn't kick Mick Jagger out of my bed,
   but I'm not a homosexual.

31   ANSWERS >

1. **FIDDLER ON THE ROOF**
   1971, USA
   Director: Norman Jewison
   Cast: (Chaim) Topol, Norma Crane, Leonard Frey
   Screenplay: Joseph Stein
   Based on the book by Sholom Aleichem

2. **REBEL WITHOUT A CAUSE**
   1955, USA
   Director: Nicholas Ray
   Cast: James Dean, Natalie Wood, Sal Mineo
   Screenplay: Nicholas Ray, Irving Shulman and Stewart Stern

3. **SLAP SHOT**
   1977, USA
   Director: George Roy
   Cast: Paul Newman, Michael Ontkean, Lindsay Crouse
   Screenplay: Nancy Dowd

4. **LIVE AND LET DIE**
   1973, UNITED KINGDOM
   Director: Guy Hamilton
   Cast: Roger Moore, Yaphet Kotto, Jane Seymour
   Screenplay: Tom Mankiewicz.
   Based on the book by Ian Fleming

5. **OCEAN'S ELEVEN**
   1960, USA
   Director: Lewis Milestone
   Cast: Frank Sinatra, Dean Martin, Sammy Davis Jr
   Screenplay: George Clayton Johnson, Jack Golden Russell,
   Harry Brown, Charles Lederer and Billy Wilder

6. **HAIR**
   1979, USA
   Director: Milos Forman
   Cast: John Savage, Treat Williams, Beverly D'Angelo
   Screenplay: Gerome Ragni, James Rado, Galt MacDermot and
   Michael Weller

1.   -Maybe you shouldn't drink so much.
      -Maybe I shouldn't breathe so much either.

2.   -His high exaltedness, the Great Jabba the Hutt,
      has decreed that you are to be terminated immediately.
      -Good, I hate long waits.

      Star Wars
      Return of the Jedi

3.   -You can turn your back on a person, but don't ever turn your
      back on a drug. Especially when it's waving a razor-sharp hunting
      knife in your eye.

4.   -Men would pay $200 for me, and here you are turning down
      a freebie. You could get a perfectly good dishwasher for that.

5.   -Have you ever seen a Commie drink a glass of water?
      -Well, I can't say I have.

6.   -A lot of holes in the desert, and a lot of problems are buried in
      those holes. But you gotta do it right. I mean, you gotta have the
      hole already dug before you show up with a package in the trunk.
      Otherwise, you're talking about a half-hour to forty-five minutes
      worth of digging. And who knows who's gonna come along in
      that time? Pretty soon, you gotta dig a few more holes.
      You could be there all fuckin' night.

    ANSWERS >

1. **LEAVING LAS VEGAS**
   1995, USA
   Director: Mike Figgis
   Cast: Nicolas Cage, Elisabeth Shue, Julian Sands
   Screenplay: Mike Figgis
   Based on the book by John O'Brien

2. **RETURN OF THE JEDI**
   1983, USA
   Director: Richard Marquand
   Cast: Mark Hamill, Harrison Ford, Carrie Fisher
   Screenplay: George Lucas and Lawrence Kasdan

3. **FEAR AND LOATHING IN LAS VEGAS**
   1998, USA
   Director: Terry Gilliam
   Cast: Johnny Depp, Benicio Del Toro, Tobey Maguire
   Screenplay: Terry Gilliam, Tony Grisoni, Tod Davies and Alex Cox
   Based on the book by Hunter S. Thompson

4. **KLUTE**
   1971, USA
   Director: Alan J Pakula
   Cast: Jane Fonda, Donald Sutherland, Charles Cioffi
   Screenplay: Andy Lewis and Dave Lewis

5. **DR STRANGELOVE OR: HOW I LEARNED TO STOP
   WORRYING AND LOVE THE BOMB**
   1963, UNITED KINGDOM
   Director: Stanley Kubrick
   Cast: Peter Sellers, George C Scott, Sterling Hayden
   Screenplay: Stanley Kubrick, Terry Southern and Peter George
   Based on the book by Peter George

6. **CASINO**
   1995, USA
   Director: Martin Scorsese
   Cast: Robert De Niro, Sharon Stone Joe Pesci
   Screenplay: Nicholas Pileggi and Martin Scorsese
   Based on the book by Nicholas Pileggi

1. Courage! What makes a king out of a slave? What makes the flag on the mast to wave? Courage. What makes the elephant charge his tusk in the misty mist, or the dusky dusk? What makes the muskrat guard his musk? Courage. What makes the sphinx the seventh wonder? Courage. What makes the dawn come up like thunder? Courage. What makes the Hottentot so hot? What puts the ape in apricot? What have they got that I ain't got--Courage!

   Wizard of Oz

2. -I don't make things difficult. That's the way they get, all by themselves.

3. -You're late.
   -You're stunning.
   -You're forgiven.

4. -I could have killed 'em all! I could kill you. In town, you're the law; out here it's me. Don't push it. Don't push it or I'll give you a war you won't believe.

5. -I thought you knew. I want to go throughout life jumping into fountains naked.

6. -Bring the dog: I love animals... I'm a great cook.

ANSWERS >

1. THE WIZARD OF OZ
   1939, USA
   Director: Victor Fleming
   Cast: Judy Garland, Ray Bolger, Bert Lahr
   Screenplay: Noel Langley, Florence Ryerson and Edgar Allan Woolf
   Based on the book by L. Frank Baum

2. LETHAL WEAPON
   1987, USA
   Director: Richard Donner
   Cast: Mel Gibson, Danny Glover, Gary Busey
   Screenplay: Shane Black

3. PRETTY WOMAN
   1990, USA
   Director: Garry Marshall
   Cast: Richard Gere, Julia Roberts, Ralph Bellamy
   Screenplay: J.F Lawton

4. FIRST BLOOD
   1982, USA
   Director: Ted Kotcheff
   Cast: Sylvester Stallone, Richard Crenna, Brian Dennehy
   Screenplay: Michael Kozoll, William Sackheim, Sylvester Stallone
   Based on the book by David Morrell

5. THE BIRDS
   1963, USA
   Director: Alfred Hitchcock
   Cast: Rod Taylor, Tippi Hedren, Jessica Tandy
   Screenplay: Daphne Du Maurier and Evan Hunter

6. FATAL ATTRACTION
   1987, USA
   Director: Adrian Lyne
   Cast: Michael Douglas, Glenn Close, Anne Archer
   Screenplay: James Dearden and Nicholas Meyer

1. -Well, I think I'll get saddled up and go lookin for a woman.
    -Good huntin'.
    -Shouldn't take more than a couple of days. I'm not picky...
    as long as she's smart...pretty...sweet...gently...and tender...
    and refined...lovely...carefree.

2. -I just want to apologize to Josh's mom, and Mike's mom,
    and my mom. I am so sorry! Because it was my fault. I was
    the one who brought them here. I was the one that said
    keep going south. I was the one who said that we were not
    lost. It was my fault, because it was my project. I am so scared!
    I don't know what's out there. We are going to die out here!
    I am so scared!

3. -Life all comes down to a few moments. This is one of them.

4. -A relationship, I think, is like a shark. You know? It has to
    constantly move forward or it dies. And I think what we got
    on our hands is a dead shark.

5. -Real diamonds! They must be worth their weight in gold!

6. -The son of a bitch is here. I saw him. I'm gonna get him.

ANSWERS >

1. **BUTCH CASSIDY AND THE SUNDANCE KID**
   1969, USA
   Director: George Roy Hill
   Cast: Paul Newman, Robert Redford, Katharine Ross
   Screenplay: William Goldman

2. **THE BLAIR WITCH PROJECT**
   1999, USA
   Director: Daniel Myrick, Eduardo Sánchez
   Cast: Heather Donahue, Joshua Leonard, Michael C. Williams
   Screenplay: Daniel Myrick, Eduardo Sánchez

3. **WALL STREET**
   1987, USA
   Director: Oliver Stone
   Cast: Michael Douglas, Charlie Sheen, Daryl Hannah
   Screenplay: Stanley Weiser and Oliver Stone

4. **ANNIE HALL**
   1977, USA
   Director: Woody Allen
   Cast: Woody Allen, Diane Keaton, Tony Roberts
   Screenplay: Woody Allen and Marshall Brickman

5. **SOME LIKE IT HOT**
   1959, USA
   Director: Billy Wilder
   Cast: Jack Lemmon, Tony Curtis, Marilyn Monroe
   Screenplay: Robert Thoeren, M. Logan, Billy Wilder and I.A.L. Diamond

6. **THE FRENCH CONNECTION**
   1971, USA
   Director: William Friedkin
   Cast: Gene Hackman, Fernando Rey, Roy Scheider
   Screenplay: Ernest Tidyman, Edward M. Keyes
   Based on the book by Robin Moore

1. -Say Lou, didya hear the one about the guy who couldn't
    afford personalized plate so he went and changed his name
    to J3L2404?
    Yah, that's a good one.

2. -You see, Danny, I can deal with the bullets, and the bombs,
    and the blood. I don't want money, and I don't want medals.
    What I do want is for you to stand there in that faggoty white
    uniform and with your Harvard mouth extend me some fucking
    courtesy. You gotta ask me nicely.

    A Few Good Men

3. -What the hell you wanna go fuck around with that river for?
    -Because it's there.
    -It's there alright. You get in there and can't get out,
    you gonna wish it wasn't.

4. -60 years old and still getting crushes on other men's wives.
    I hope that when I'm your age, I'll be a little bit smarter than that.
    -You sure are off to a slow start.

5. I'll feed you, I'll dress you in the morning, I'll undress
    you at night...I'll take care of you.

6. -The only thing we had in common was that she was from Iowa,
    and I had once heard of Iowa.

ANSWERS >

1.   FARGO
      1996, USA
      Director: Joel Coen
      Cast: Frances McDormand, William H Macy, Steve Buscemi
      Screenplay: Joel Coen and Ethan Coen

2.   A FEW GOOD MEN
      1992, USA
      Director: Rob Reiner
      Cast: Tom Cruise, Jack Nicholson, Demi Moore
      Screenplay: Aaron Sorkin

3.   DELIVERANCE
      1972, USA
      Director: John Boorman
      Cast: Jon Voight, Burt Reynolds, Ned Beatty
      Screenplay: James Dickey
      Based on the book by James Dickey

4.   NOBODY'S FOOL
      1994, USA
      Director: Robert Benton
      Cast: Paul Newman, Jessica Tandy, Bruce Willis
      Screenplay: Robert Benton
      Based on the book by Richard Russo

5.   NINE 1/2 WEEKS
      1986, USA
      Director: Adrian Lyne
      Cast: Mickey Rourke, Kim Basinger, Margaret Whitton
      Screenplay:Sarah Kernandan, Zalman King, Patricia Louisianna Knop
      Based on the book by Elizabeth McNeill

6.   FIELD OF DREAMS
      1989, USA
      Director: Phil Alden Robinson
      Cast: Kevin Costner, Amy Madigan, Gaby Hoffman
      Screenplay: Phil Alden Robinson
      Based on the book W.P. Kinsella

1. -I don't believe that God made man in his image. 'Cause most of the shit that happens comes from man. Now, I think man was made in the Devil's image, and women were created out of God's. 'Cause after all, women can have babies, which is kind of like creating. And which also counts for the fact that women are so attracted to men... 'cause let's face it... the Devil is a hell of a lot more interesting! So the whole point in life is for men and women to get married... so that God and the Devil can get together and work it out.

2. -I'll make him an offer he can't refuse.

3. -You're a big man, but you're out of shape.
    With me it's a full time job. Now behave yourself.

4. -I'm a connoisseur of roads. I've been tasting roads my whole life. This road will never end. It probably goes all around the world.

5. -I was murdered, an unnatural death, and now I walk the earth in limbo until the werewolf's curse is lifted.

6. -I should have given you to God when you were born, but I was weak and backslidin'.

ANSWERS >

1. THE WITCHES OF EASTWICK
    1987, USA
    Director: George Miller
    Cast: Jack Nicholson, Cher, Susan Sarandon
    Screenplay: Michael Cristofer
    Based on the book by John Updike

2. THE GODFATHER
    1972, USA
    Director: Francis Ford Coppola
    Cast: Marlon Brando, Al Pacino, James Caan
    Screenplay: Mario Puzo and Francis Ford Coppola
    Based on the book by Mario Puzo

3. GET CARTER
    1971, UNITED KINGDOM
    Director: Mike Hodges
    Cast: Michael Caine, Ian Hendry, Britt Ekland
    Screenplay: Mike Hodges
    Based on the book by Ted Lewis (III)

4. MY OWN PRIVATE IDAHO
    1991, USA
    Director: Gus Van Sant
    Cast: River Phoenix, Keanu Reeves, James Russo
    Screenplay: Gus Van Sant

5. AN AMERICAN WEREWOLF IN LONDON
    1981, USA
    Director: John Landis
    Cast: David Naughton, Jenny Agutter, Griffin Dunne
    Screenplay: John Landis

6. CARRIE
    1976, USA
    Director: Brian De Palma
    Cast: Sissy Spacek, Piper Laurie, William Katt
    Screenplay: Lawrence D. Cohen.
    Based on the book by Stephen King

1. -Don't worry! As long as you hit that wire with the connecting hook at precisely eighty-eight miles per hour the instant the lightning strikes the tower ... everything will be fine!

   Back to the Future

2. -They was giving me ten thousand watts a day, you know, and I'm hot to trot! The next woman takes me on's gonna light up like a pinball machine and pay off in silver dollars!

3. -The 70s are dead and gone. The 80s are going to be something wonderfully new and different, and so am I.

4. -The light that burns twice as bright burns half as long and you have burned so very, very brightly, Roy.

5. -I think you should send us the biggest transport plane you have, and take this thing to the Arctic or somewhere and drop it where it will never thaw.

6. -Soul is the music people understand. Sure it's basic and it's simple, but it's something else because it's honest. That's it. It sticks its neck out and says it straight from the heart. Sure there's a lot of different music you can get off on but soul is more than that. It grabs you by the bollocks and lifts you above the shite.

ANSWERS >

1. **BACK TO THE FUTURE**
   1985, USA
   Director: Robert Zemeckis
   Cast: Michael J Fox, Christopher Lloyd, Crispin Glover
   Screenplay: Robert Zemeckis and Bob Gale

2. **ONE FLEW OVER THE CUCKOO'S NEST**
   1975, USA
   Director: Milos Forman
   Cast: Jack Nicholson, Louise Fletcher, Brad Dourif
   Screenplay. Bo Goldman and Lawrence Hauben
   Based on the book by Ken Kesey

3. **CAN'T STOP THE MUSIC**
   1980, USA
   Director: Nancy Walker
   Cast: Alex Briley, David Hodo, Glenn Hughes
   Screenplay: Alan Carr, Bronte Woodard

4. **BLADE RUNNER**
   1982, USA
   Director: Ridley Scott
   Cast: Harrison Ford, Rutger Hauer, Sean Young
   Screenplay: Hampton Fancher, David Webb Peoples, Roland Kibbee
   Based on the book by Philip K. Dick

5. **THE BLOB**
   1958, USA
   Director:Irwin S. Yeaworth Jr.
   Cast: Steve McQueen, Aneta Corsaut, Earl Rowe
   Screenplay: Kay Linaker, Irwing H. Millgate

6. **THE COMMITMENTS**
   1991, UNITED KINGDOM
   Director: Alan Parker
   Cast: Robert Arkins, Michael Aherne, Angeline Ball
   Screenplay: Dick Clement, Ian La Frenais and Roddy Doyle
   Based on the book by Roddy Doyle

1. -All of you! You all killed him! And my brother, and Riff.
   Not with bullets, or guns. With hate. Well, now I can kill,
   too, because now I have hate!

   West Side Story

2. -There's nothing more irresistible to a man than a woman
   who's in love with him.

3. -For a nation of pigs, it sures seems funny that you don't eat
   them! Jesus Christ forgave the bastards, but I can't! I hate!
   I hate you! I hate your nation! And I hate your people!
   And I fuck your sons and daughters because they're pigs!
   You're all pigs!

4. -Geology is the study of pressure and time. Thats all it takes,
   really. Pressure... and time. That, and big goddamn poster.

5. -I'd say the odds against a successful escape are about 100 to
   one. But may I add another word, Colonel? The odds against
   survival in this camp are even worse.

6. -Loneliness has followed me my whole life. Everywhere.
   In bars, in cars, sidewalks, stores, everywhere. There's
   no escape. I'm God's lonely man.

ANSWERS >

1.   WEST SIDE STORY
     1961, USA
     Director: Robert Wise, Jerome Robbins
     Cast: Natalie Wood, Richard Beymer, George Chakiris
     Screenplay: Jerome Robbins, Arthur Laurents and Ernest Lehman
     Based on the play Romeo and Juliet by William Shakespeare

2.   THE SOUND OF MUSIC
     1965, USA
     Director: Robert Wise
     Cast: Julie Andrews, Christopher Plummer, Eleanor Parker
     Screenplay: Ernest Lehman, Richard Rodgers and
     Oscar Hammerstein II, Howard Lindsay and Russel Crouse

3.   MIDNIGHT EXPRESS
     1978, UNITED KINGDOM
     Director: Alan Parker
     Cast: Brad Davis, Irene Miracle, Bo Hopkins
     Screenplay: Oliver Stone
     Based on the book by Billy Hayes and William Hoffer

4.   THE SHAWSHANK REDEMPTION
     1994, USA
     Director: Frank Darabont
     Cast: Tim Robbins, Morgan Freeman, Bob Gunton
     Screenplay: Frank Darabont
     Based on the book by Stephen King

5.   THE BRIDGE ON THE RIVER KWAI
     1957, UNITED KINGDOM
     Director: David Lean
     Cast: William Holden, Alec Guinness, Jack Hawkins
     Screenplay: Michael Wilson, Carl Foreman
     Based on the book by Pierre Boulle

6.   TAXI DRIVER
     1976, USA
     Director: Martin Scorsese
     Cast: Robert De Niro, Cybill Shepherd, Harvey Keitel
     Screenplay: Paul Schrader

1.   I'm sure it comes as no great suprise to you when I say that
      there are little corners in everyone which were better off left
      alone; sicknesses, weaknesses, which should never be exposed.
      But... that's your stock in trade, isn't it - a man's weakness?
      And I was never really fully aware of mine... Until you brought
      them out.

2.   -We'll make a great team, old man. You for the words,
      me for the pictures. I can be your eyes.

3.   -You wanna see dry land. You really wanna see it?
      I'll take you there.

4.   -We must be like the ox, and have no thought, except for the
      Party. And have no love, but for the Angka. People starve, but
      we must not grow food. We must honor the comrade children,
      whose minds are not corrupted by the past.

5.   -It ain't so easy to shoot a man anyhow, especially if the
      son-of-a-bitch is shootin' back at you.

6.   -We all dream of being a child again, even the worst of us.
      Perhaps the worst most of all.

1. **KLUTE**
   1971, USA
   Director: Alan J Pakula
   Cast: Jane Fonda, Donald Sutherland, Charles Cioffi
   Screenplay: Andy Lewis and Dave Lewis

2. **THE YEAR OF LIVING DANGEROUSLY**
   1983, AUSTRALIA
   Director: Peter Weir
   Cast: Mel Gibson, Linda Hunt, Sigourney Weaver
   Screenplay: C.J. Kand, Peter Weir and David Williamson
   Based on the book by C.J. Kand

3. **WATERWORLD**
   1995, USA
   Director: Kevin Reynolds
   Cast: Kevin Costner, Dennis Hopper, Jeanne Tripplehorn
   Screenplay: Peter Rader and David Twohy

4. **THE KILLING FIELDS**
   1984, UNITED KINGDOM
   Director: Roland Joffe
   Cast: Sam Waterston, Haing S Ngor, John Malkovich
   Screenplay: Bruce Robinson

5. **UNFORGIVEN**
   1992, USA
   Director: Clint Eastwood
   Cast: Clint Eastwood, Gene Hackman, Morgan Freeman
   Screenplay: David Webb Peoples

6. **THE WILD BUNCH**
   1969, USA
   Director: Sam Peckinpah
   Cast: William Holden, Ernest Borgnine, Robert Ryan
   Screenplay: Walon Green, Roy N. Sickner, Walon Green and
   Sam Peckinpah

1. -Would ya just watch the hair? Ya know, I spend a long time on my hair and he hit it; he hit my hair.

2. -What do they call you?
   -Some call me one thing and others another.
   -What do they call you the most?
   -My name.

3. -I have no plans to call on you, Clarice, the world being more interesting with you in it. Be sure you extend me the same courtesy.

   Silence of the Lambs

4. -I'm not going to shoot you in the state you're in.
   -State of what? State of California? I know where the fuck I am, Jack.

5. -I'm not a fool, Plissken!
   -Call me Snake.

6. -You've got to remember that these are just simple farmers. These are people of the land. The common clay of the new West. You know... morons.

1.   SATURDAY NIGHT FEVER
        1977, USA
        Director: John Badham
        Cast: John Travolta, Karen Lynn Gorney, Barry Miller
        Screenplay: Nik Cohn and Norman Wexler

2.   RED RIVER
        1948, USA
        Director: Howard Hawks
        Cast: John Wayne, Montgomery Clift, Walter Brennan
        Screenplay: Borden Chase, Borden Chase and Charles Schnee

3.   THE SILENCE OF THE LAMBS
        1991, USA
        Director: Jonathan Demme
        Cast: Jodie Foster, Anthony Hopkins, Scott Glenn
        Screenplay: Ted Tally
        Based on the book by Thomas Harris

4.   BOOGIE NIGHTS
        1997, USA
        Director: Paul Thomas Anderson
        Cast: Mark Wahlberg, Burt Reynolds, Julianne Moore
        Screenplay: Paul Thomas Anderson

5.   ESCAPE FROM NEW YORK
        1981, USA
        Director: John Carpenter
        Cast: Kurt Russell, Lee Van Cleef, Ernest Borgnine
        Screenplay: John Carpenter and Nick Castle

6.   BLAZING SADDLES
        1973, USA
        Director: Mel Brooks
        Cast: Cleavon Little, Gene Wilder, Harvey Korman
        Screenplay: Andrew Bergman, Mel Brooks, Richard Pryor,
        Norman Steinberg and Alan Uger

1. -Nervous?
    -Yes.
    -First time?
    -No, I've been nervous lots of times.

2. -There are ways of telling whether she is a witch.
    -Are there? Oh well, tell us!
    -Tell me. What do you do with witches?
    -Burn them!
    -And what do you burn, apart from witches?
    -More witches!
    -Wood!
    -Now, why do witches burn?
    -...because they're made of... wood?
    -Good. So how do you tell whether she is made of wood?
    -Build a bridge out of her!
    -But don't we also build bridges out of stone?
    -Oh yeah.

    Monty Python and the Holy Grail

3. -That's more than a dress. That's an Audrey Hepburn movie.

4. -I tried to capture the spirit of the thing.

5. -Up in the sky, look! It's a bird! It's a plane!

    Superman

6. -The rest is silence.

1.   AIRPLANE! / FLYING HIGH
     1980, USA
     Director: Jim Abrahams, David Zucker, Jerry Zucker
     Cast: Robert Hays, Julie Hagerty, Robert Stack
     Screenplay: Jim Abrahams, David Zucker and Jerry Zucker

2.   MONTY PYTHON AND THE HOLY GRAIL
     1974, UNITED KINGDOM
     Director: Terry Gilliam, Terry Jones
     Cast: Graham Chapman, John Cleese, Terry Gilliam
     Screenplay: Graham Chapman, John Cleese, Eric Idle, Terry Gilliam,
     Terry Jones and Michael Palin

3.   JERRY MAGUIRE
     1996, USA
     Director: Cameron Crowe
     Cast: Tom Cruise, Cuba Gooding Jr, Renee Zellweger
     Screenplay: Cameron Crowe

4.   SLAP SHOT
     1977, USA
     Director: George Roy
     Cast: Paul Newman, Michael Ontkean, Lindsay Crouse
     Screenplay: Nancy Dowd

5.   SUPERMAN
     1941, USA
     Director: Dave Fleischer
     Cast: Bud Collyer (voice), Joan Alexander (voice)
     Screenplay: Seymour Kneitel, Joe Shuster

6.   HAIR
     1979, USA
     Director: Milos Forman
     Cast: John Savage, Treat Williams, Beverly D'Angelo
     Screenplay: Gerome Ragni, James Rado, Galt MacDermot and
     Michael Weller

1.　-You don't understand how i feel. I'm standing there with my pants down, and my CROTCH slung out for the world to see, and you're tellin' me that's the best you can do! Well if that's your best, then your best sucks... now, I don't care what you got for selling me out but i sure as shit hope its worth it!

2.　-Isn't that your phone number?
-Is it? I don't call myself that often.

3.　-Imagine that! Seven million people all wanting to live together. New York must be the friendliest place there is.

4.　-You must have shot an awful lot of tigers, Sir.
-Yes, I used a machine-gun.

5.　-The only performance that will satisfy you is when I play dead.
-Your very next role! You'll be quite convincing, I assure you.

6.　-He's just doing it to get a rise out of you. Just ignore him.
-Sweets, you couldn't ignore me if you tried.
-So... so. Are you guys like boyfriend-girlfriend? Steady dates? Lovers? Come on, Sporto, level with me. Do you slip her the hot beef injection?

ANSWERSS >

1.   **CITIZEN KANE**
     1941, USA
     Director: Orson Welles
     Cast: Orson Welles, Joseph Cotten, Everett Sloane
     Screenplay: Herman J. Mankiewicz, Orson Welles and
     John Houseman.

2.   **CHINATOWN**
     1974, USA
     Director: Roman Polanski
     Cast: Jack Nicholson, Faye Dunaway, John Huston
     Screenplay: Robert Towne and Roman Polanski

3.   **CROCODILE DUNDEE**
     1986, AUSTRALIA
     Director: Peter Faiman
     Cast: Paul Hogan, Linda Kozlowski, John Meillon
     Screenplay: John Cornell, Paul Hogan and Ken Shadie

4.   **THE ITALIAN JOB**
     1969, UNITED KINGDOM
     Director: Peter Collinson
     Cast: Michael Caine, Noel Coward, Maggie Blye
     Screenplay: Troy Kennedy-Martin

5.   **NORTH BY NORTHWEST**
     1959, USA
     Director: Alfred Hitchcock
     Cast: Cary Grant, Eva Marie Saint, James Mason
     Screenplay: Ernest Lehman

6.   **THE BREAKFAST CLUB**
     1985, USA
     Director: John Hughes
     Cast: Emilio Esteves, Judd Nelson, Molly Ringwald
     Screenplay: John Hughes

1. -A fellow will remember a lot of things you wouldn't think he'd
    remember. You take me. One day, back in 1896, I was crossing
    over to Jersey on the ferry, and as we pulled out, there was
    another ferry pulling in, and on it there was a girl waiting to get off.
    A white dress she had on. She was carrying a white parasol.
    I only saw her for one second. She didn't see me at all, but I'll bet
    a month hasn't gone by since that I haven't thought of that girl.

    Citizen Kane

2. -Why don't you kiss her instead of talking her to death?
    -You want me to kiss her, huh?
    -Ah, youth is wasted on the wrong people!

    It's a wonderful Life

3. -What a fitting end to your life's pursuits. You're about to become
    a permanent addition to this archaeological find. Who knows?
    In a thousand years, even you may be worth something.

4. -Yippee-ki-yay, motherfucker!

    Die Hard

5. -Look speghetti arms. This is my dance space. This is your
    dance space. I don't go into yours, you don't go into mine.
    You gotta hold the frame.

6. -We were all feeling a bit shagged and fagged and fashed,
    it being a night of no small expenditure.

ANSWERS >

1. CITIZEN KANE
   1941, USA
   Director: Orson Welles
   Cast: Orson Welles, Joseph Cotten, Everett Sloane
   Screenplay: Herman J. Mankiewicz, Orson Welles and
   John Houseman.

2. IT'S A WONDERFUL LIFE
   1946, USA
   Director: Frank Capra
   Cast: James Stewart, Donna Reed, Lionel Barrymore
   Screenplay: Philip Van Doren Stern, Frances Goodrich,
   Albert Hackett, Frank Capra, Jo Swerling and Michael Wilson

3. RAIDERS OF THE LOST ARK
   1981, USA
   Director: Steven Spielberg
   Cast: Harrison Ford, Karen Allen, Wolf Kahler
   Screenplay: George Lucas, Philip Kaufman and Lawrence Kasdan

4. DIE HARD
   1988, USA
   Director: John McTiernan
   Cast: Bruce Willis, Alan Rickman, Bonnie Bedelia
   Screenplay: Jeb Stuart and Steven E. de Souza
   Based on the book by Roderick Thorp

5. DIRTY DANCING
   1987, USA
   Director: Emile Ardolino
   Cast: Jennifer Grey, Patrick Swayze, Jerry Orbach
   Screenplay: Eleanor Bergstein

6. A CLOCKWORK ORANGE
   1971, USA
   Director: Stanley Kubrick
   Cast: Malcolm McDowell, Patrick Magee, Adrienne Corri
   Screenplay: Stanley Kubrick.
   Based on the book by Anthony Burgess

1. -Cargo and ship destroyed. I should reach the frontier in about 6 weeks. With a little luck, the network will pick me up. This is Ripley, last survivor of the Nostromo, signing off.

    Alien

2. -Antony is dead? You say that as if it were a everyday occurence. The soup is hot, the soup is cold. Antony is alive, Antony is dead.

    Cleopatra

3. -Well, what am I supposed to do? You won't answers my calls. You change your number. I mean, I'm not gonna be ignored, Dan!

4. -I don't have to take this abuse from you. I've got hundreds of people dying to abuse me.

5. -The thing about a shark, it's got lifeless eyes, black eyes, like a doll's eyes. When it comes at you it doesn't seem to be livin'... until he bites you, and those black eyes - roll over white.

    Jaws

6. -How's east?
    -East?
    -Yeah, we've been going south all this time. How's east?
    -Wicked Witch of the West, Wicked Witch of the East. Which one was bad?
    -Wicked Witch of the West was the bad one.
    -Then we should go east.

ANSWERS >

1.   **ALIEN**
     1979, USA
     Director: Ridley Scott
     Cast: Tom Skerritt, Sigourney Weaver, John Hurt
     Screenplay: Dan O'Bannon, Ronald Shusett, Dan O'Bannon,
     David Giler and Walter Hill

2.   **CLEOPATRA**
     1963, USA
     Director: Joseph L Mankiewicz
     Cast: Elizabeth Taylor, Richard Burton, Rex Harrison
     Screenplay: Sidney Buchman, Ben Hecht, Ranald MacDougall and
     Joseph L. Mankiewicz
     Based on the book by Carlo Mario Franzero

3.   **FATAL ATTRACTION**
     1987, USA
     Director: Adrian Lyne
     Cast: Michael Douglas, Glenn Close, Anne Archer
     Screenplay: James Dearden and Nicholas Meyer.

4.   **GHOSTBUSTERS**
     1984, USA
     Director: Ivan Reitman
     Cast: Bill Murray, Dan Aykroyd, Harold Ramis
     Screenplay: Dan Aykroyd, Harold Ramis and Rick Moranis

5.   **JAWS**
     1975, USA
     Director: Steven Spielberg
     Cast: Roy Scheider, Robert Shaw, Richard Dreyfuss
     Screenplay: Peter Benchley, Carl Gottlieb, John Milius, Howard Sackler
     and Robert Shaw
     Based on the book by Peter Benchley

6.   **THE BLAIR WITCH PROJECT**
     1999, USA
     Director: Daniel Myrick, Eduardo Sánchez
     Cast: Heather Donahue, Joshua Leonard, Michael C. Williams
     Screenplay: Daniel Myrick, Eduardo Sánchez

1. -Gareth used to prefer funerals to weddings. He said it was
    easier to get enthusiastic about a ceremony one had an outside
    chance of eventually being involved in.

2. -Oh, waiter!
    -That is not a waiter, my dea. That is a butler.
    -Well, I can't yell Oh, butler! can I? Maybe somebody's name
    is Butler.
    -You have a point. An idiotic one, but a point.

3. -It's so clean out here!
    -That's because they don't throw their garbage away.
    They turn it into television shows.

4. -I didn't want to do this, but I'm afraid I'm gonna have to pull
    rank on you. I'm with the Mattress Police. There are no tags
    on these mattresses.

5. -It's like, how much more black could this be? And the answers
    is none. None more black.

6. -A senatorial hearing has a way of catapulting everyone involved
    into the public eye with a subsequent effect on one's career.
    It'll be a pleasure to have you along.

1.   **FOUR WEDDINGS AND A FUNERAL**
     1994, UNITED KINGDOM
     Director: Mike Newell
     Cast: Hugh Grant, Andie MacDowell, Kristin Scott Thomas
     Screenplay: Richard Curtis

2.   **ALL ABOUT EVE**
     1950, USA
     Director: Joseph L Mankiewicz
     Cast: Bette Davis, Anne Baxter, George Sanders
     Screenplay: Joseph L. Mankiewicz and Mary Orr

3.   **ANNIE HALL**
     1977, USA
     Director: Woody Allen
     Cast: Woody Allen, Diane Keaton, Tony Roberts
     Screenplay: Woody Allen and Marshall Brickman

4.   **FLETCH**
     1985, USA
     Director: Michael Ritchie
     Cast: Chevy Chase, Dana Wheeler Nicholson, Tim Matheson
     Screenplay: Andrew Bergman
     Based on the book by Gregory McDonald

5.   **THIS IS SPINAL TAP**
     1984, USA
     Director: Rob Reiner
     Cast: Michael McKean, Christopher Guest, Harry Shearer
     Screenplay: Christopher Guest, Michael McKean, Rob Reiner and
     Harry Shearer

6.   **BULLITT**
     1968, USA
     Director: Peter Yates
     Cast: Steve Mcqueen, Robert Vaughn, Jacqueline Bisset
     Screenplay: Alan Trustman and Harry Kleiner
     Based on the book by Robert L. Pike

1. -I know what you're thinking. Did he fire six shots or only five? Well, to tell you the truth, in all this excitement, I've kinda lost track myself. But, being as this is a .44 Magnum, the most powerful handgun in the world, and would blow your head clean off, you've got to ask yourself one question:
Do I feel lucky? Well, do ya punk?

   Dirty Harry

2. -You never really understand a person until you consider things from his point of view: until you climb inside of his skin and walk around in it.

   To Kill A Mockingbird

3. -You want answerss?
   -I think I'm entitled.
   -You want answerss?
   -I want the truth!
   -You can't handle the truth!

   A Few Good Men

4. -Your eyes are full of hate, forty-one. That's good.
Hate keeps a man alive.

5. -Nobody puts baby in a coner.

   Dirty Dancing

ANSWERS >

1.	DIRTY HARRY
	1971, USA
	Director: Don Siegal
	Cast: Clint Eastwood, Harry Guardino, Reni Santoni
	Screenplay: Harry Julian Fink, Rita M. Fink, Dean Riesner and
	John Milius

2.	TO KILL A MOCKINGBIRD
	1962, USA
	Director: Robert Mulligan
	Cast: Gregory Peck, Mary Badham, Philip Alford
	Screenplay: Horton Foote. Based on the book by Harper Lee

3.	A FEW GOOD MEN
	1992, USA
	Director: Rob Reiner
	Cast: Tom Cruise, Jack Nicholson, Demi Moore
	Screenplay: Aaron Sorkin

4.	BEN-HUR
	1959, USA
	Director: William Wyler
	Cast: Charlton Heston, Jack Hawkins, Stephen Boyd
	Screenplay: Karl Tunberg, Maxwell Anderson, Christopher Fry and
	Gore Vidal. Based on the book by Lew Wallace

5.	DIRTY DANCING
	1987, USA
	Director: Emile Ardolino
	Cast: Jennifer Grey, Patrick Swayze, Jerry Orbach
	Screenplay: Eleanor Bergstein

1. -Don't you think I realize what's going on here, Miss? Who do you think I am, huh? Don't you think I know that if I was some hotshot from out of town that pulled inside here and you guys made a reservation mistake, I'd be the first one to get a room and I'd be upstairs relaxing right now? But I'm not some hotshot from out of town. I'm a small reporter from Rolling Stone magazine that's in town to do an exclusive interview with Michael Jackson that's gonna be picked up by every major magazine in the country. I was gonna call the article Michael Jackson Is Sitting On Top of the World, but now I think I might as well just call it Michael Jackson Can Sit On Top of the World Just As Long As He Doesn't Sit in the Beverly Palm Hotel 'Cause There's No Niggers Allowed in There!

2. -The whole thing stinks like yesterday's diapers!

3. -I can't lie to you about your chances, but......
    you have my sympathies.

4. -A heart can be broken, but it will keep beating just the same.

5. -Come on, now. Don't be naive, Lieutenant. We both know how careers are made. Integrity is something you sell the public.

6. -Let them hate me. So long as they fear me!

1. BEVERLY HILLS COP
    1984, USA
    Director: Martin Brest
    Cast: Eddie Murphy, Judge Reinhold, John Ashton
    Screenplay: Danilo Bach and Daniel Petrie Jr.

2. WHO FRAMED ROGER RABBIT
    1988, USA
    Director: Robert Zemeckis
    Cast: Bob Hoskins, Christopher Lloyd, Joanna Cassidy
    Screenplay: Jeffrey Price and Peter S. Seaman
    Based on the book by Gary K. Wolf

3. ALIEN
    1979, USA
    Director: Ridley Scott
    Cast: Tom Skerritt, Sigourney Weaver, John Hurt
    Screenplay: Dan O'Bannon, Ronald Shusett, Dan O'Bannon,
    David Giler and Walter Hill

4. FRIED GREEN TOMATOES
    1991, USA
    Director: Jon Avnet
    Cast: Kathy Bates, Jessica Tandy, Mary Stuart Masterson
    Screenplay: Carol Sobieski, Fannie Flagg
    Based on the book by Fannie Flagg

5. BULLITT
    1968, USA
    Director: Peter Yates
    Cast: Steve Mcqueen, Robert Vaughn, Jacqueline Bisset
    Screenplay: Alan Trustman and Harry Kleiner
    Based on the book by Robert L. Pike

6. CALIGULA
    1980, ITALY/USA
    Director: Tinto Brass
    Cast: Malcolm McDowell, Peter O'Toole, Teresa Ann Savoy
    Screenplay: Gore Vidal, Bob Guccione, Giancarlo Lui,
    Masolino D'Amico, Franco Rossellini and Roberto Rossellini

1.   -I was to extract one decagram of miolyn from four tons
      of earthworms.
      -Really?
      -Yes. I was on that project for five years. I was the only one
      who believed in it, everyone else said it couldn't be done.
      -It can't.
      -I know that now. I proved it.

2.   -Whose motorcycle is this?
      -It's a chopper, baby.
      -Whose chopper is this?
      -It's Zed's.
      -Who's Zed?
      -Zed's dead, baby. Zed's dead.

3.   -Do you have any illegal substances in the vehicle?
      -Not anymore, man.

4.   -What do you all do for fun around here? listen to
      the grass grow?

5.   -It's a Sicilian message.
      It means Luca Brasi sleeps with the fishes.

6.   -Every day above ground is a good day.

ANSWERS >

1.   **AWAKENINGS**
   1990, USA
   Director: Penny Marshall
   Cast: Robert De Niro, Robin Williams, Julie Kavner
   Screenplay: Steven Zaillian. Based on the book by Oliver Sacks

2.   **PULP FICTION**
   1994, USA
   Director: Quentin Tarantino
   Cast: John Travolta, Samuel L Jackson, Uma Thurman
   Screenplay: Quentin Tarantino and Roger Avary

3.   **UP IN SMOKE**
   1978, USA
   Director: Lou Adler
   Cast: Cheech Marin, Tommy Chong, Stacy Keach
   Screenplay: Tommy Chong and Cheech Marin

4.   **BONNIE AND CLYDE**
   1967, USA
   Director: Arthur Penn
   Cast: Warren Beatty, Faye Dunaway, Michael J Pollard
   Screenplay: David Newman (III), Robert Benton and Robert Towne

5.   **THE GODFATHER**
   1972, USA
   Director: Francis Ford Coppola
   Cast: Marlon Brando, Al Pacino, James Caan
   Screenplay: Mario Puzo and Francis Ford Coppola
   Based on the book by Mario Puzo

6.   **SCARFACE**
   1983, USA
   Director: Brian De Palma
   Cast: Al Pacino, Steven Bauer, Michelle Pfeiffer
   Screenplay: Oliver Stone and Howard Hawks
   Based on the book by Armitage Trail

1. -What's forget about it?
   -Forget about it is like if you agree with someone, you know,
   like Raquel Welch is one great piece of ass, forget about it. But
   then, if you disagree, like A Lincoln is better than a Cadillac?
   Forget about it! You know? But then, it's also like if something's
   the greatest thing in the world, like mingia those peppers, forget
   about it. But it's also like saying Go to hell! too. Like, you know,
   like Hey Paulie, you got a one inch pecker? and Paulie says
   Forget about it! Sometimes it just means forget about it.

2. -Have you no fear, English?
   -My fear is my concern.

3. -I will not be threatened by a walking meat loaf!

4. -I know now that my wife has become host to a Candarian
   demon. I fear that the only way to stop those possessed by the
   spirits of the book is through the act of...bodily dismemberment.

5. -Do you know what she did, your cunting daughter?

6. -I just can't take no pleasure in killing. There's just some
   things you gotta do. Don't mean you have to like it.

1. **DONNIE BRASCO**
   1997, USA
   Director: Mike Newell
   Cast: Al Pacino, Johnny Depp, Michael Madsen
   Screenplay: Paul Attanasio
   Based on the book by Joseph D. Pistone and Richard Woodley

2. **LAWRENCE OF ARABIA**
   1962, UNITED KINGDOM
   Director: David Lean
   Cast: Peter O'Toole, Alec Guinness, Anthony Quinn
   Screenplay: T.E. Lawrence, Robert Bolt and Michael Wilson

3. **AN AMERICAN WEREWOLF IN LONDON**
   1981, USA
   Director: John Landis
   Cast: David Naughton, Jenny Agutter, Griffin Dunne
   Screenplay: John Landis

4. **THE EVIL DEAD**
   1983, USA
   Director: Sam Raimi
   Cast: Bruce Campbell, Ellen Sandweiss, Hal Delrich
   Screenplay: Sam Raimi

5. **THE EXORCIST**
   1973, USA
   Director: William Friedkin
   Cast: Ellen Burstyn, Max Von Sydow, Linda Blair
   Screenplay: William Peter Blatty

6. **THE TEXAS CHAINSAW MASSACRE**
   1974, USA
   Director: Tobe Hopper
   Cast: Marilyn Burns, Gunner Hansen, Ed Neal
   Screenplay: Kim Henkel and Tobe Hooper

1. -Of course, you know, certain skeptics note that perhaps 10,000 of the nations's most elite highway patrolmen are out there waiting for us after we start, but let's stay positive: think of the fact that there's not one state in the 50 that has the death penalty for speeding...although I'm not so sure about Ohio.

2. -Look, your worshipfulness, let's get one thing straight. I take orders from just one person: Me!
    -It's a wonder you're still alive.

    Star Wars A New Hope

3. -For God's sake, Chris! The whole world is watching. We can't let him die in front of a live audience!
    -He was born in front of a live audience.

4. -I think I need a root canal. I definitely need a long, slow root canal.

5. -Try to get this straight. There is nothing between us. There has never been anything between us. Just air.

6. -What's your name? Come on. What's your name? Do you have a name? Do you have a police record? Where are you from?
    -Disneyland.

ANSWERS >

1.   **THE CANNONBALL RUN**
   1981, USA
   Director: Hal Needham
   Cast: Burt Reynolds, Roger Moore, Farrah Fawcett
   Screenplay: Brock Yates

2.   **STAR WARS**
   1977, USA
   Director: George Lucas
   Cast: Mark Hamill, Harrison Ford, Carrie Fisher
   Screenplay: George Lucas

3.   **THE TRUMAN SHOW**
   1998, USA
   Director: Peter Weir
   Cast: Jim Carrey, Laura Linney, Ed Harris
   Screenplay: Andrew Niccol

4.   **LITTLE SHOP OF HORRORS**
   1986, USA
   Director: Frank Oz
   Cast: Rick Moranis, Ellen Greene, Vincent Gardenia
   Screenplay: Charles B. Griffith and Howard Ashman

5.   **SINGIN' IN THE RAIN**
   1952, USA
   Director: Gene Kelly, Stanley Donen
   Cast: Gene Kelly, Debbie Reynolds, Donald O'Conner
   Screenplay: Betty Comden and Adolph Green

6.   **THE HITCHER**
   1986, USA
   Director: Robert Harmon
   Cast: Rutger Hauer, C Thomas Howell, Jennifer Jason Leigh
   Screenplay: Eric Red

1. -Now, there's only two reasons why you didn't sit on that step next to me. Either you too scared, boy, or you just hate niggers. What is it boy - you too scared?
    -Naahh, I just hate niggers.

2. -Some birds aren't meant to be caged. Their feathers are just too bright.

3. -Listen. Why don't we begin with what happened tonight, hmm? Perhaps you could...you know, give me some of the details.
    -I was here, Doc...died, you came.
    -That's it?
    -I'm a demon for details.

4. -Keaton once said, I don't believe in God, but I'm afraid of him. Well I believe in God, and the only thing that scares me is Keyser Soze.

5. -Why don't you knock it off with them negative waves? Why don't you dig how beautiful it is out here? Why don't you say something righteous and hopeful for a change?

    Kelly's Heroes

6. -Time marches on and sooner or later, you realize it is marchin' across your face.

ANSWERS >

1. ESCAPE FROM ALCATRAZ
    1979, USA
    Director: Donald Siegel
    Cast: Clint Eastwood, Patrick McGoohan, Roberts Blossom
    Screenplay: Richard Tuggle
    Based on the book by J. Campbell Bruce

2. THE SHAWSHANK REDEMPTION
    1994, USA
    Director: Frank Darabont
    Cast: Tim Robbins, Morgan Freeman, Bob Gunton
    Screenplay: Frank Darabont
    Based on the book by Stephen King

3. MARATHON MAN
    1976, USA
    Director: John Schlesinger
    Cast: Dustin Hoffman, Laurence Olivier, Roy Scheider
    Screenplay: Robert Towne and William Goldman
    Based on the book by William Goldman

4. THE USUAL SUSPECTS
    1995, USA
    Director: Bryan Singer
    Cast: Stephen Baldwin, Gabriel Byrne, Chazz Palminteri
    Screenplay: Christopher McQuarrie

5. KELLY'S HEROES
    1970, USA
    Director: Brian G Hutton
    Cast: Clint Eastwood, Telly Savalas, Don Rickles
    Screenplay: Troy Kennedy-Martin

6. STEEL MAGNOLIAS
    1989, USA
    Director: Herbert Ross
    Cast: Sally Field, Dolly Parton, Julia Roberts
    Screenplay: Robert Harling

1. -I'm a star. I'm a fucking star.

2. -You gonna kill me now, Snake?
    -I'm too tired. Maybe later.

3. -Who's that there?
    -I don't know. Must be a king.
    -Why?
    -He hasn't got shit all over him.

    Monty Python and the Holy Grail

4. -You know where you're going?
    -Uptown, I believe?
    -Uptown? You headed into Harlem!
    -Well you just stay on the tail of that jukebox and there's
    an extra twenty dollars in it for you.
    -Hey man, for twenty bucks, I'd take you to a Ku Klux Klan
    cookout!

5. -Now comes the part where I relieve you, the little people, of
    the burden of your failed and useless lives. But remember, as
    my plastic surgeon always said: if you gotta go, go with a smile.

6. -You guys got nothing to worry about. I'm a professional.
    -A professional what?

ANSWERS >

1. **BOOGIE NIGHTS**
   1997, USA
   Director: Paul Thomas Anderson
   Cast: Mark Wahlberg, Burt Reynolds, Julianne Moore
   Screenplay: Paul Thomas Anderson

2. **ESCAPE FROM NEW YORK**
   1981, USA
   Director: John Carpenter
   Cast: Kurt Russell, Lee Van Cleef, Ernest Borgnine
   Screenplay: John Carpenter and Nick Castle

3. **MONTY PYTHON AND THE HOLY GRAIL**
   1974, UNITED KINGDOM
   Director: Terry Gilliam, Terry Jones
   Cast: Graham Chapman, John Cleese, Terry Gilliam
   Screenplay: Graham Chapman, John Cleese, Eric Idle, Terry Gilliam,
   Terry Jones and Michael Palin

4. **LIVE AND LET DIE,**
   1973, UNITED KINGDOM
   Director: Guy Hamilton
   Cast: Roger Moore, Yaphet Kotto, Jane Seymour
   Screenplay: Tom Mankiewicz.
   Based on the book by Ian Fleming

5. **BATMAN**
   1989, USA
   Director: Tim Burton
   Cast: Jack Nicholson, Michael Keaton, Kim Basinger
   Screenplay: Bob Kane, Sam Hamm and Warren Skaaren

6. **FERRIS BUELLER'S DAY OFF**
   1986, USA
   Director: John Hughes
   Cast: Matthew Broderick, Alan Ruck, Mia Sara
   Screenplay: John Hughes

1.　　-You wanna go for a ride?
　　　-No, thanks.
　　　-No, thanks. What does that mean?
　　　-I don't want to go.
　　　-Go where?
　　　-On a ride.
　　　-A ride? Hell, that's a good idea. Okay, let's go. Hey, let's go.

2.　　-A drugged person can learn to cope with seeing their dead
　　　grandmother crawling up their leg with a knife in her teeth.
　　　But no one should be asked to handle this trip.

3.　　-Hollis seems to think you're an innocent man.
　　　-Well, I've been accused of a lot of things before,
　　　Mrs. Mulwray, but never that.

4.　　-You were only supposed to blow the bloody doors off.

5.　　-You are not machines! You are men! With the love of humanity
　　　in your hearts! Don't hate! Only the unloved hate; the unloved and
　　　the unnatural. Soldiers!

6.　　-Hey, hey, hey, baby! What do you say?
　　　-Don't say anything and we'll get along just fine.

　　　　　　　　　　　ANSWERS >

1.   BLUE VELVET
       1986, USA
       Director: David Lynch
       Cast: Kyle MacLachlan, Isabella Rossellini, Dennis Hopper
       Screenplay: David Lynch

2.   FEAR AND LOATHING IN LAS VEGAS
       1998, USA
       Director: Terry Gilliam
       Cast: Johnny Depp, Benicio Del Toro, Tobey Maguire
       Screenplay: Terry Gilliam, Tony Grisoni, Tod Davies and Alex Cox
       Based on the book by Hunter S. Thompson

3.   CHINATOWN
       1974, USA
       Director: Roman Polanski
       Cast: Jack Nicholson, Faye Dunaway, John Huston
       Screenplay: Robert Towne and Roman Polanski

4.   THE ITALIAN JOB
       1969, UNITED KINGDOM
       Director: Peter Collinson
       Cast: Michael Caine, Noel Coward, Maggie Blye
       Screenplay: Troy Kennedy-Martin

5.   THE GREAT DICTATOR
       1940, USA
       Director: Charles Chaplin
       Cast: Charles Chaplin, Jack Oakie, Reginald Gardiner
       Screenplay: Charles Chaplin

6.   AMERICAN GRAFFITI
       1973, USA
       Director: George Lucas
       Cast: Richard Dreyfuss, Ronny Howard, Paul LeMat
       Screenplay: George Lucas, Gloria Katz and Willard Huyck

1. -Even a poisonous snake isn't bad. You just have to keep away
    from the sharp end.

2. -Luke, you *can* destroy the Emperor. He has foreseen this.
    Join me, and together we will rule the galaxy as father and son!

    Star Wars The Empire Strikes Back

3. -You don't understand. I coulda had class. I coulda been a
    contender. I coulda been somebody, instead of a bum. Which
    is what I am, let's face it. It was you, Charley.

    On the waterfront

4. -I was married for four years, and pretended to be happy. And I
    had six years of analysis, and pretended to be sane. My husband
    ran off with his boyfriend, and I had an affair with my analyst, who
    told me I was the worst lay he'd ever had.

5. -I think voting is the opium of the masses in this country.
    Every four years you deaden the pain.

6. -Now hold it, hold it. We're about to accuse Haldeman,
    who only happens to be the second most important man in
    this country, of conducting a criminal conspiracy from inside
    the White House. It would be nice if we were right.

    All the President's Men

ANSWERS >

1. **THE GODS MUST BE CRAZY**
   1980, BOTSWANA
   Director: Jamie Uys
   Cast: Marius Weyers, Sandra Prinsloo, N!xau
   Screenplay: Jamie Uys

2. **THE EMPIRE STRIKES BACK**
   1980, USA
   Director: Irwin Kershner
   Cast: Mark Hamill, Harrison Ford, Carrie Fisher
   Screenplay: George Lucas, Leigh Brackett and Lawrence Kasdan

3. **WATERFRONT**
   1950 UNITED KINGDOM
   Director: Michael Anderson
   Cast: Robert Newton, Kathleen Harrison
   Screenplay: John Brophy, Paul Soskin

4. **NETWORK**
   1976, USA
   Director: Sidney Lumet
   Cast: William Holden, Faye Dunaway, Peter Finch
   Screenplay: Paddy Chayefsky

5. **REDS**
   1981, USA
   Director: Warren Beatty
   Cast: Warren Beatty, Diane Keaton, Edward Herrmann
   Screenplay: Warren Beatty, Trevor Griffiths, Elaine May, John Reed (II),
   Jeremy Pikser and Peter S. Feibleman

6. **ALL THE PRESIDENTS MEN**
   1976, USA
   Director: Alan J Pakula
   Cast: Robert Redford, Dustin Hoffman, Jason Robards
   Screenplay: William Goldman
   Based on the book by Carl Bernstein and Bob Woodward

1. -A good fight should be like a small play but played seriously.
   When the opponent expands, I contract. When he contracts,
   I expand. And when the opportunity presents itself, I do not hit!
   It hits all by itself.

2. -Who are these men?
   -They're associated with Special Forces.
   -What? What does that mean?
   -It means that they are associated with Special Forces.

3. -We're not students, were The Ramones.

4. -Oh, the Indian is hot. I go for exotic types, especially
   when they're half-naked.
   -Lulu!
   -You tell him I'll make up for all the indignities they suffered
   in Roots..

5. -Don't take that tone with me, young man!
   I fought the war for your sort.
   -I bet you're sorry you won.

6. -Well, I've always believed that if done properly, armed
   robbery doesn't have to be an unpleasant experience.

1. **ENTER THE DRAGON**
   1973, USA
   Director: Robert Clouse
   Cast: Bruce Lee, John Saxon, Jim Kelly
   Screenplay: Michael Allin

2. **NO WAY OUT**
   1987, USA
   Director: Roger Donaldson
   Cast: Kevin Costner, Gene Hackman, Sean Young
   Screenplay: Robert Garland.
   Based on the book by Kenneth Fearing

3. **ROCK 'N' ROLL HIGH SCHOOL**
   1979, USA
   Director: Allan Arkush, Joe Dante
   Cast: P.J Soles, Vincent van Patten, Clint Howard
   Screenplay: Richard Whitley, Russ Dronch

4. **CAN'T STOP THE MUSIC**
   1980, USA
   Director: Nancy Walker
   Cast: Alex Briley, David Hodo, Glenn Hughes
   Screenplay: Alan Carr, Bronte Woodard

5. **A HARD DAY'S NIGHT**
   1964, UNITED KINGDOM
   Director: Richard Lester
   Cast: John Lennon, Paul McCartney, George Harrison
   Screenplay: Alun Owen

6. **THELMA & LOUISE**
   1991, USA
   Director: Ridley Scott
   Cast: Susan Sarandon, Geena Davis, Harvey Keitel
   Screenplay: Callie Khouri

1. -I am awake.
    -Your eyes are shut.
    -Who you gonna believe?

2. -But what is so alarming about laughter?
    -Laughter kills fear, and without fear there can be no faith,
    because without fear of the Devil there is no more need of God.

3. -When you love someone, you've gotta trust them. There's
    no other way. You've got to give them the key to everything
    that's yours. Otherwise, what's the point? And, for a while,
    I believed that's the kind of love I had.

4. -He's a man from outer space and we're taking him
    to his spaceship.
    -Well, can't he just beam up?
    -This is REALITY, Greg.

5. -Like the sign says, speed's just a question of money.
    How fast can you go?

6. -I should have killed myself when he took me. After the first
    time, before we were married, Ralph promised never again.
    He promised me and I believed him. But sin never dies.
    Sin never dies.

ANSWERS >

1. **MILLER'S CROSSING**
   1990, USA
   Director: Joel Coen
   Cast: Gabriel Byrne, Albert Finney, Marcia Gay Harden
   Screenplay: Joel Coen and Ethan Coen
   Based on the book by Dashiell Hammett

2. **THE NAME OF THE ROSE**
   1986, FRANCE/ITALY/WEST GERMANY
   Director: Jean Jacques Annaud
   Cast: Sean Connery, F Murray Abraham, Christian Slater
   Screenplay: Andrew Birkin, Gérard Brach, Howard Franklin and
   Alain Godard
   Based on the book by Umberto Eco

3. **CASINO**
   1995, USA
   Director: Martin Scorsese
   Cast: Robert De Niro, Sharon Stone Joe Pesci
   Screenplay: Nicholas Pileggi and Martin Scorsese
   Based on the book by Nicholas Pileggi

4. **E.T THE EXTRA-TERRESTRIAL**
   1982, USA
   Director: Steven Spielberg
   Cast: Dee Wallace, Henry Thomas, Peter Coyote
   Screenplay: Melissa Mathison

5. **MAD MAX**
   1979, AUSTRALIA
   Director: George Miller
   Cast: Mel Gibson, Joanne Samuel, Hugh Keays Byrne
   Screenplay: James McCausland and George Miller

6. **CARRIE**
   1976, USA
   Director: Brian De Palma
   Cast: Sissy Spacek, Piper Laurie, William Katt
   Screenplay: Lawrence D. Cohen
   Based on the book by Stephen King

1. -Is there something bad here?
    -Well, you know, Doc, when something happens, you can leave
    a trace of itself behind. Say like, if someone burns toast. Well,
    maybe things that happen leave other kinds of traces behind.
    Not things that anyone can notice, but things that people who
    shine can see.

2. -You've got to believe me, Officer! He is coming to Haddonfield.
    Because I know him - I'm his doctor! You must be ready for him.
    If you don't, it's your funeral!

3. -Queen Elizabeth is a man! Prince Charles is a pervert!
    Winston Churchill was full of shit! Shakespeare's French!

4. -Why are you laughing?
    -You're going to rent cars?!
    -That's right, I know a lot about cars. I've been stealing
    them since I was 14.

5. -Keep talking, Matty. Experience has shown that I can be
    convinced of anything.

6. -There are watchers in this world, and there are doers.
    And the watchers sit around watching the doers do.
    Tonight you watched, and I did.

ANSWERS >

1. THE SHINING
   1980, USA
   Director: Stanley Kubrick
   Cast: Jack Nicholson, Shelley Duvall, Danny Lloyd
   Screenplay: Stanley Kubrick and Diane Johnson
   Based on the book by Stephen King

2. HALLOWEEN
   1978, USA
   Director: John Carpenter
   Cast: Donald Pleasence, Jamie Lee Curtis, Nancy Loomis
   Screenplay: John Carpenter and Debra Hill

3. AN AMERICAN WEREWOLF IN LONDON
   1981, USA
   Director: John Landis
   Cast: David Naughton, Jenny Agutter, Griffin Dunne
   Screenplay: John Landis

4. CARLITO'S WAY
   1993, USA
   Director: Brian De Palma
   Cast: Al Pacino, Sean Penn, Penelope Ann Miller
   Screenplay: David Koepp
   Based on the book by Edwin Torres

5. BODY HEAT
   1981, USA
   Director: Lawrence Kasdan
   Cast: William Hurt, Kathleen Turner, Richard Crenna
   Screenplay: Lawrence Kasdan

6. BAREFOOT IN THE PARK
   1967, USA
   Director: Gene Saks
   Cast: Robert Redford, Jane Fonda, Charles Boyer
   Screenplay: Neil Simon

1. -Speed is like a dozen transatlantic flights without ever getting off the plane. Time change. You lose, you gain. Makes no difference so long as you keep taking the pills. But sooner or later, you've got to get out because it's crashing, and then all at once the frozen hours melt out through the nervous system and seep out the pores.

2. -Normally, both of you would be dead as fucking fried chicken by now, but since I'm in a transitional period, I don't want to kill either one of your asses.

3. -Most people don't know how they're gonna feel from one moment to the next. But a dope fiend has a pretty good idea. All you gotta do is look at the labels on the little bottles.

4. -He's pissed at YOU, Wirf.
   -Only because he knows I won't go away.
   -I know how he feels.

5. -This is your life and it's ending one minute at a time.

6. -Do you just want to lose weight, or are you looking to increase strength and flexibility as well?
   -I want to look good naked!

ANSWERS >

1. **WITHNAIL AND I**
    1986, UNITED KINGDOM
    Director: Bruce Robinson
    Cast: Richard E Grant, Paul McGann, Richard Griffiths
    Screenplay: Bruce Robinson

2. **PULP FICTION**
    1994, USA
    Director: Quentin Tarantino
    Cast: John Travolta, Samuel L Jackson, Uma Thurman
    Screenplay: Quentin Tarantino and Roger Avary

3. **DRUGSTORE COWBOY**
    1989, USA
    Director: Gus Van Sant
    Cast: Matt Dillon, Kelly Lynch, James Remar
    Screenplay: Gus Van Sant, Daniel Yost and William S. Burroughs
    Based on the book by James Fogle

4. **NOBODY'S FOOL**
    1994, USA
    Director: Robert Benton
    Cast: Paul Newman, Jessica Tandy, Bruce Willis
    Screenplay: Robert Benton
    Based on the book by Richard Russo

5. **FIGHT CLUB**
    1999, USA
    Director: David Fincher
    Cast: Brad Pitt, Edward Norton, Helena Bonham Carter
    Screenplay: Jim Uhls
    Based on the book by Chuck Palahniuk

6. **AMERICAN BEAUTY**
    1999, USA
    Director: Sam Mendes
    Cast: Kevin Spacey, Annette Bening, Thora Birch
    Screenplay: Alan Ball

1. -Hawkeye Pierce? I got a twix from headquarters about
   you. Says you stole a jeep.
   -No, sir, no. I didn't steal it. No, it's right outside.

   M*A*S*H

2. -I would suggest that those of us with stout hearts
   and trim waistlines, start using the stairs.
   -That's 135 floors.
   -All downhill.

3. -I saw a young officer on deck the other day, and he looked
   DAMN familiar... even with his clothes on!
   -So... he recognized ya, so?
   -So doesn't that bother you?
   -If it bothered me, I wouldn't have married ya.
   -Well, first you arrested me six times!
   -Well, I had to figure out some way to keep you off the streets
   until you'd marry me!

4. -I'm loud, darling, but never cheap.

5. -At birth, I was cast into a flaming pit of scum forgotten by God.

6. -Neighbors bring food with death, and flowers with sickness,
   and little things in between.

ANSWERS >

1. MASH
    1970, USA
    Director: Robert Altman
    Cast: Donald Sutherland, Elliott Gould, Tom Skerritt
    Screenplay: Ring Lardner Jr.
    Based on the book by Richard Hooker

2. THE TOWERING INFERNO
    1974, USA
    Director: John Guillermin, Irwin Allen
    Cast: Steve Mcqueen, Paul Newman, William Holden
    Screenplay: Stirling Silliphant
    Based on the book by Richard Martin Stern, Thomas N. Scortia and
    Frank M. Robinson

3. THE POSEIDON ADVENTURE
    1972, USA
    Director: Ronald Neame
    Cast: Gene Hackman, Ernest Borgnine, Red Buttons
    Screenplay: Wendell Mayes and Stirling Silliphant
    Based on the book by Paul Gallico

4. THE CRYING GAME
    1992, UNITED KINGDOM
    Director: Neil Jordan
    Cast: Stephan Rea, Miranda Richardson, Forest Whitaker
    Screenplay: Neil Jordan

5. NATURAL BORN KILLERS
    1994, USA
    Director: Oliver Stone
    Cast: Woody Harrelson, Juliette Lewis, Robert Downey Jr.
    Screenplay: Quentin Tarantino, David Veloz, Richard Rutowski and
    Oliver Stone

6. TO KILL A MOCKINGBIRD
    1962, USA
    Director: Robert Mulligan
    Cast: Gregory Peck, Mary Badham, Philip Alford
    Screenplay: Horton Foote
    Based on the book by Harper Lee.

1. -You know, we are sitting here like a couple of regular fellows, and if I have to go out there and put you down, I tell you, I won't like it. But, if it's between you and some poor bastard whose wife you're gonna turn into a widow, buddy, you are going down.
    -There is a flip side to this coin. What if you do get me boxed in and I will have to put you down? Cause no matter what, you will not get in my way. We've been face to face, yeah. But I will not hesitate, not for a second.

2. -We split the car.
    -How the fuck do you split a car, you dummy? With a fucking chainsaw?

3. -I'm a marked man in this department. For what?
    -I've already arranged a transfer for you.
    -To where? China?

4. Go ahead, punk, make my day.

    Dirty Harry

5. -Water polo, isn't that dangerous?
    -It sure is. I had two ponies drowned under me.

6. -The mirror...it's broken!
    -Yes, I know. I like it that way. Makes me look the way I feel.

ANSWERS >

1. **HEAT**
    1995, USA
    Director: Michael Mann
    Cast: Al Pacino, Robert De Niro, Val Kilmer
    Screenplay: Michael Mann

2. **FARGO**
    1996, USA
    Director: Joel Coen
    Cast: Frances McDormand, William H Macy, Steve Buscemi
    Screenplay: Joel Coen and Ethan Coen

3. **SERPICO**
    1973, USA
    Director: Sidney Lumet
    Cast: Al Pacino, John Randolph, Jack Kehoe
    Screenplay: Waldo Salt and Norman Wexler
    Based on the book by Peter Maas

4. **DIRTY HARRY**
    1971, USA
    Director: Don Siegal
    Cast: Clint Eastwood, Harry Guardino, Reni Santoni
    Screenplay: Harry Julian Fink, Rita M. Fink, Dean Riesner and
    John Milius

5. **SOME LIKE IT HOT**
    1959, USA
    Director: Billy Wilder
    Cast: Jack Lemmon, Tony Curtis, Marilyn Monroe
    Screenplay: Robert Thoeren, M. Logan, Billy Wilder and
    I.A.L. Diamond

6. **THE APARTMENT**
    1960, USA
    Director: Billy Wilder
    Cast: Jack Lemmon, Shirley MacLaine, Fred MacMurray
    Screenplay: Billy Wilder and I.A.L. Diamond

1. -Ahem, look. Sorry, sorry. I just, ahem. Well, this is a very stupid question and..., particularly in view of our recent shopping excursion, but I just wondered, by any chance, ahem, eh, I mean obviously not because I guess I've only slept with 9 people, but-but I-I just wondered... ehh. I really feel, ehh, in short, to recap it slightly in a clearer version, eh, the words of David Cassidy in fact, eh, while he was still with the Partridge family, eh, I think I love you, and eh, I-I just wondered by any chance you wouldn't like to...eh... eh... no, no, no of course not... I'm an idiot, he's not... Excellent, excellent. Fantastic. Eh, I was gonna say lovely to see you, sorry to disturb... better get on...
   -That was very romantic.
   -Well, I thought it over a lot, you know, I wanted to get it just right.

2. -I love you more than any woman's ever loved a rabbit.

3. -They drew first blood, not me. They drew first blood.

4. -She's wonderful! Where did you find her?
   -976-BABE.

5. -Now I have a machine gun. Ho ho ho.

6. -I don't mind a reasonable amount of trouble.

91

1. **FOUR WEDDINGS AND A FUNERAL**
   1994, UNITED KINGDOM
   Director: Mike Newell
   Cast: Hugh Grant, Andie MacDowell, Kristin Scott Thomas
   Screenplay: Richard Curtis

2. **WHO FRAMED ROGER RABBIT**
   1988, USA
   Director: Robert Zemeckis
   Cast: Bob Hoskins, Christopher Lloyd, Joanna Cassidy
   Screenplay: Jeffrey Price and Peter S. Seaman
   Based on the book by Gary K. Wolf

3. **FIRST BLOOD**
   1982, USA
   Director: Ted Kotcheff
   Cast: Sylvester Stallone, Richard Crenna, Brian Dennehy
   Screenplay: Michael Kozoll, William Sackheim, Sylvester Stallone
   Based on the book by David Morrell

4. **PRETTY WOMAN**
   1990, USA
   Director: Garry Marshall
   Cast: Richard Gere, Julia Roberts, Ralph Bellamy
   Screenplay: J.F Lawton

5. **DIE HARD**
   1988, USA
   Director: John McTiernan
   Cast: Bruce Willis, Alan Rickman, Bonnie Bedelia
   Screenplay: Jeb Stuart and Steven E. de Souza
   Based on the book by Roderick Thorp

6. **THE MALTESE FALCON**
   1941, USA
   Director: John Huston
   Cast: Humphrey Bogart, Mary Astor, Peter Lorre
   Screenplay: John Huston
   Based on the book by Dashell Hammett

1. -Hey look, mister. We serve hard drinks in here for men who want to get drunk fast and we don't need any characters around to give the joint atmosphere. Is that clear, or do I have to slip you my left for a convincer?

2. -Where were you last night?
    -That's so long ago, I don't remember.
    -Will I see you tonight?
    -I never make plans that far ahead.

3. -Can you imagine the life he must have had?
    -Yes, I believe I can.
    -No, I don't believe so. I don't think any of us can.

4. -Doesn't it hurt?
    -Well, I sort of lay there in pain, but I love it. I really love it. I lay there hovering between consciousness and unconsciousness. It's really the greatest.

5. -Are you suicidal?
    -Only in the mornings.

    Ocean's
    Eleven

6. -Oh no, you can't take my photograph.
    -Oh, I'm sorry, you believe it will take your spirit away?
    -No, you got the lens cap on.

    Crocodile Dundee

93   ANSWERS >

1. **IT'S A WONDERFUL LIFE**
   1946, USA
   Director: Frank Capra
   Cast: James Stewart, Donna Reed, Lionel Barrymore
   Screenplay: Philip Van Doren Stern, Frances Goodrich, Albert
   Hackett, Frank Capra, Jo Swerling and Michael Wilson

2. **CASABLANCA**
   1942, USA
   Director: Michael Curtiz
   Cast: Humphrey Bogart, Ingrid Bergman, Paul Henreid
   Screenplay: Murray Burnett, Joan Alison, Julius J. Epstein,
   Philip G. Epstein, Howard K and, Casey Robinson

3. **THE ELEPHANT MAN**
   1980, USA
   Director: David Lynch
   Cast: Anthony Hopkins, John Hurt, Anne Bancroft
   Screenplay: Christopher De Vore, Eric Bergren and David Lynch
   Based on the book by Sir Frederick Treves and Ashley Montagu

4. **LOLITA,**
   1962, UNITED KINGDOM
   Director: Stanley Kubrick
   Cast: James Mason, Shelley Winters, Peter Sellers
   Screenplay: Vladimir Nabokov and Stanley Kubrick
   Based on the book by Vladimir Nabokov

5. **OCEAN'S ELEVEN**
   1960, USA
   Director: Lewis Milestone
   Cast: Frank Sinatra, Dean Martin, Sammy Davis Jr
   Screenplay: George Clayton Johnson, Jack Golden Russell,
   Harry Brown, Charles Lederer and Billy Wilder

6. **CROCODILE DUNDEE**
   1986, AUSTRALIA
   Director: Peter Faiman
   Cast: Paul Hogan, Linda Kozlowski, John Meillon
   Screenplay: John Cornell, Paul Hogan and Ken Shadie

1.   -We had two bags of grass, seventy-five pellets of mescaline, five
     sheets of high powered blotter acid, a salt shaker half full of
     cocaine and a whole galaxy of multicolored uppers, downers,
     screamers, laughers...Also a quart of tequilla, a quart of rum,
     a case of budweiser, a pint of raw ether, and two dozen amyls.
     But the only thing that worried me was the ehter. There is nothing
     in the world more helpless and irresponsible than a man in the
     depths of an ether binge. And i knew we'd get into that rotten
     stuff pretty soon.

2.   -You know something, Verna? If I turn my back for long enough
     for Big Ed to put a hole in it, there'd be a hole in it.

3.   -God is not on our side because he hates idiots, also.

4.   Life moves pretty fast. If you don't stop and look
     around once in a while, you could miss it.

5.   -You know, you guys are amazing. You think not getting
     caught in a lie is the same thing as telling the truth!

6.   -Saayyy! Nice beaver!
     -Thanks. I just had it stuffed.

ANSWERS >

1. **FEAR AND LOATHING IN LAS VEGAS**
    1998, USA
    Director: Terry Gilliam
    Cast: Johnny Depp, Benicio Del Toro, Tobey Maguire
    Screenplay: Terry Gilliam, Tony Grisoni, Tod Davies and Alex Cox
    Based on the book by Hunter S. Thompson

2. **WHITE HEAT**
    1949, USA
    Director: Raoul Walsh
    Cast: James Cagney, Virginia Mayo, Edmond O'Brien
    Screenplay: Virginia Kellogg, Ivan Goff and Ben Roberts

3. **A FISTFULL OF DOLLARS**
    1964, ITALY
    Director: Sergio Leone
    Cast: Clint Eastwood, Marianne Kand, Gian maria Volonté
    Screenplay: A. Bonzzoni, Victor Andrés Catena

4. **FERRIS BUELLER'S DAY OFF**
    1986, USA
    Director: John Hughes
    Cast: Matthew Broderick, Alan Ruck, Mia Sara
    Screenplay: John Hughes

5. **THREE DAYS OF THE CONDOR**
    1975, USA
    Director: Sydney Pollack
    Cast: Robert Redford, Faye Dunaway, Cliff Robertson
    Screenplay: Lorenzo Semple Jr and David Rayfiel
    Based on the book by James Grady

6. **THE NAKED GUN:**
    FROM THE FILES OF POLICE SQUAD
    1988, USA
    Director: David Zucker
    Cast: Leslie Nielsen, George Kennedy, Priscilla Presley
    Screenplay: Jim Abrahams, David Zucker and Pat Proft

1. -I think now, looking back, we did not fight the enemy. We fought ourselves. The enemy was in us. The war is over for me now, but it will always be there, the rest of my days. As I'm sure Elias will be, fighting with Barnes for what Rhah called possession of my soul. There are times since, I've felt like a child, born of those two fathers. But be that as it may, those of us who did make it have an obligation to build again. To teach to others what we know, and to try with what's left of our lives to find a goodness and a meaning to this life.

2. -Alright. I'll do it. I'will show you how a Prussian officer fights.
    -And I will show you where the Iron Crosses grow.

3. -The greatest trick the devil ever pulled was convincing the world he didn't exist.

4. -You make me sick with your heroics. There's a stench of death about you. You carry it in your pack like the plague.

5. -My mother told me to never do this.

6. -She just goes a little mad sometimes. We all go a little mad sometimes. Haven't you?

ANSWERS >

1. **PLATOON**
   1986, USA
   Director: Oliver Stone
   Cast: Tom Berenger, Willem Dafoe, Charlie Sheen
   Screenplay: Oliver Stone

2. **CROSS OF IRON**
   1977, UNITED KINGDOM/WESTGERMANY
   Director: Sam Peckinpah
   Cast: James Coburn, Maximilian Schell, James Mason
   Screenplay: Julius J. Epstein, James Hamilton and Walter Kelley
   Based on the book by Frederick Forsyth

3. **THE USUAL SUSPECTS**
   1995, USA
   Director: Bryan Singer
   Cast: Stephen Baldwin, Gabriel Byrne, Chazz PalMinteri
   Screenplay: Christopher McQuarrie

4. **THE BRIDGE ON THE RIVER KWAI**
   1957, UNITED KINGDOM
   Director: David Lean
   Cast: William Holden, Alec Guinness, Jack Hawkins
   Screenplay: Michael Wilson, Carl Foreman
   Based on the book by Pierre Boulle

5. **THE HITCHER**
   1986, USA
   Director: Robert Harmon
   Cast: Rutger Hauer, C Thomas Howell, Jennifer Jason Leigh
   Screenplay: Eric Red

6. **PSYCHO**
   1960, USA
   Director: Alfred Hitchcook
   Cast: Anthony Perkins, Janet Leigh, Vera Miles
   Screenplay: Joseph Stefano
   Based on the book by Robert Bland

1. -I only have sex with a guy for money.
    -Yeah, I know.
    -And two guys can't love each other.
    -Yeah. Well, I don't know. I mean....I mean for me, I could love
    someone even if I, you know, wasn't paid for it. I love you
    and....you don't pay me.

2. -And maybe there's no peace in this world. For us or for anyone
    else, I don't know. But I do know that, as long as we live, we
    must remain true to ourselves.

3. -You wanna know how you do it? Here's how, they pull a knife,
    you pull a gun. He sends one of yours to the hospital, you send
    on of his to the morgue! That's the Chicago way, and that's how
    you get Capone. Now, do you want to do that? Are you ready to
    do that?

    The Untouchables

4. -You'll live with the stink of the streets all your life.
    -I like the stink of the streets. It cleans out my lungs.
    And it gives me a hard-on.

5. -You don't make up for your sins in church. You do it in the
    streets. You do it at home. The rest is bullshit and you know it.

6. -A favor will kill you faster than a bullet.

1.   MY OWN PRIVATE IDAHO
     1991, USA
     Director: Gus Van Sant
     Cast: River Phoenix, Keanu Reeves, James Russo
     Screenplay: Gus Van Sant

2.   SPARTACUS
     1960, USA
     Director: Stanley Kubrick
     Cast: Kirk Douglas, Laurence Olivier, Jean Simmons
     Screenplay: Dalton Trumbo, Calder Willingham and Peter Ustinov
     Based on the book by Howard Fast

3.   THE UNTOUCHABLES
     1987, USA
     Director: Brian De Palma
     Cast: Kevin Costner, Sean Connery, Charles Martin Smith
     Screenplay: David Mamet
     Based on the book by Oscar Fraley and Eliot Ness and Paul Robsky

4.   ONCE UPON A TIME IN AMERICA
     1984, USA
     Director: Sergio Leone
     Cast: Robert De Niro, James Woods, Elizabeth McGovern
     Screenplay: Leonardo Benvenuti, Piero De Bernardi, Enrico Medioli,
     Franco Arcalli, Franco Ferrini, Sergio Leone, Stuart Kaminsky and
     Ernesto Gastaldi
     Based on the book by Harry Grey

5.   MEAN STREETS
     1973, USA
     Director: Martin Scorsese
     Cast: Robert De Niro, Harvey Keitel, David Proval
     Screenplay: Martin Scorsese and Mardik Martin

6.   CARLITO'S WAY
     1993, USA
     Director: Brian De Palma
     Cast: Al Pacino, Sean Penn, Penelope Ann Miller
     Screenplay: David Koepp
     Based on the book by Edwin Torres

1. -What if I were to call the police and tell them there's a bloke staying in me hotel that's planning to shoot somebody?
   -You wouldn't do that.
   .-Why not?
   -Because I know you wear purple underwear.
   -And what's that supposed to mean?
   -Think about it.

2. -I know it was you, Fredo. You broke my heart. You broke my heart. You broke my heart.

3. -What's your last name?
   -Same as my mother's and father's.
   -And what's that?
   -Which one? My mother's or my father's?
   -Either!
   -The same as mine!

4. -I always like a little pussy after lunch.

5. -Did you lose your mind all at once, or was it a slow, gradual process?

ANSWERS >

1.   **GET CARTER**
    1971, UNITED KINGDOM
    Director: Mike Hodges
    Cast: Michael Caine, Ian Hendry, Britt Ekland
    Screenplay: Mike Hodges
    Based on the book by Ted Lewis

2.   **THE GODFATHER PART II**
    1974, USA
    Director: Francis Ford Coppola
    Cast: Al Pacino, Robert De Niro, Robert Duvall,
    Screenplay: Mario Puzo and Francis Ford Coppola

3.   **XANADU**
    1980, USA
    Director: Robert Greenwald
    Cast: Olivia Newton John, Gene Kelly, Michael Beck
    Screenplay: Richard Christian Danus and Marc Reid Rubel

4.   **THE WITCHES OF EASTWICK**
    1987, USA
    Director: George Miller
    Cast: Jack Nicholson, Cher, Susan Sarandon
    Screenplay: Michael Cristofer
    Based on the book by John Updike

5.   **THE FISHER KING**
    1991, USA
    Director: Terry Gilliam
    Cast: Robin Williams, Jeff Bridges, Amanda Plummer
    Screenplay: Richard LaGravenese

1. -Nobody's been seen coming in or out for 3 years.
   Except every morning there are 9 empty cans of tuna fish
   sitting outside the door.
   -Who do you suppose lives there?
   -Sounds like a big cat with a can opener.

2. -Picture the best orgasm you ever had. Multiply it by
   a thousand and you're still nowhere near it.

3. -You're a very strange person, Robert. I mean, what would it
   come to? If a person has no love for himself, no respect for him
   self, no love of his friends, family, work, something.
   -How can he ask for love in return? I mean, why should he ask
   for it?

4. -I wonder how such a degenerated person ever reached a
   position of authority in the Army Medical Corps!
   -He was drafted.

   M*A*S*H

5. -Miriam! I have to take your blood pressure!
   -I've been sitting still for 25 years. You missed your chance.

6. -A woman has her feelings.
   -But, Dil, you're not a woman!
   -Details, baby! Details!

          ANSWERS >

1.   BAREFOOT IN THE PARK
     1967, USA
     Director: Gene Saks
     Cast: Robert Redford, Jane Fonda, Charles Boyer
     Screenplay: Neil Simon

2.   TRAINSPOTTING
     1996, UNITED KINGDOM
     Director: Danny Boyle
     Cast: Ewan McGregor, Ewan Bremmer, Jonny Lee Miller
     Screenplay: John Hodge
     Based on the book by Irvine Welsh

3.   FIVE EASY PIECES
     1970, USA
     Director: Bob Rafelson
     Cast: Jack Nicholson, Karen Black, Billy Green
     Screenplay: Carole Eastman and Bob Rafelson

4.   MASH
     1970, USA
     Director: Robert Altman
     Cast: Donald Sutherland, Elliott Gould, Tom Skerritt
     Screenplay: Ring Lardner Jr.
     Based on the book by Richard Hooker

5.   AWAKENINGS
     1990, USA
     Director: Penny Marshall
     Cast: Robert De Niro, Robin Williams, Julie Kavner
     Screenplay: Steven Zaillian
     Based on the book by Oliver Sacks

6.   THE CRYING GAME
     1992, UNITED KINGDOM
     Director: Neil Jordan
     Cast: Stephan Rea, Miranda Richardson, Forest Whitaker
     Screenplay: Neil Jordan

1. -Once upon a time, a woman was picking up firewood.
   She came upon a poisonous snake frozen in the snow.
   She took the snake home and nursed it back to health.
   One day the snake bit her on the cheek. As she lay dying,
   she asked the snake, Why have you done this to me?
   And the snake answersed, Look, bitch, you knew I was
   a snake..

2. -Frank, let's face it. Who can trust a cop who don't
   take money?

3. -I come from a musical family.
   -My father was a famous conductor
   -Where did your father conduct?
   -On the Baltimore & Ohio.

4. -I used to live like Robinson and Crusoe, shipwrecked among 8
   million people, but one day I saw a footprint in the sand and there
   you were.

5. -There comes a time that a piano realizes that it has
   not written a concerto.

6. -The point is, Ladies and Gentlemen, that greed, for lack of
   a better word, is good. Greed is right. Greed works.

   Wall Street

ANSWERS >

1. NATURAL BORN KILLERS
    1994, USA
    Director: Oliver Stone
    Cast: Woody Harrelson, Juliette Lewis, Robert Downey Jr
    Screenplay: Quentin Tarantino, David Veloz, Richard Rutowski and
    Oliver Stone

2. SERPICO
    1973, USA
    Director: Sidney Lumet
    Cast: Al Pacino, John Randolph, Jack Kehoe
    Screenplay: Waldo Salt and Norman Wexler
    Based on the book by Peter Maas

3. SOME LIKE IT HOT
    1959, USA
    Director: Billy Wilder
    Cast: Jack Lemmon, Tony Curtis, Marilyn Monroe
    Screenplay: Robert Thoeren, M. Logan, Billy Wilder and
    I.A.L. Diamond

4. THE APARTMENT
    1960, USA
    Director: Billy Wilder
    Cast: Jack Lemmon, Shirley MacLaine, Fred MacMurray
    Screenplay: Billy Wilder and I.A.L. Diamond

5. ALL ABOUT EVE
    1950, USA
    Director: Joseph L Mankiewicz
    Cast: Bette Davis, Anne Baxter, George Sanders
    Screenplay: Joseph L. Mankiewicz and Mary Orr

6. WALL STREET
    1987, USA
    Director: Oliver Stone
    Cast: Michael Douglas, Charlie Sheen, Daryl Hannah
    Screenplay: Stanley Weiser and Oliver Stone

1. -Class isn't something you buy. Look at you. You've got on
   a 500-dollar suit and you're still a low-life.
   -Yeah, but I look good.

2. -Then you jump first.
   -No, I said.
   -What's the matter with you?
   -I can't swim.
   -Why you crazy? The fall will probably kill you.

   Butch Cassidy and The Sundance Kid

3. -Try to imagine all life as you know it stopping instantaneously
   and every molecule in your body exploding at the speed of light.

4. -What we were after now was the old surprise visit.
   That was a real kick, and good for laughs and lashings
   of the old ultraviolence.

5. -He's got a client who shot his wife in the head six times.
   Six times. Can you imagine it? I mean, even twice would be
   overdoing it, don't you think?

6. -We're more likely to believe a respected local businessman
   than some foul-mouth jerk from out of town.
   -Foul-Mouth? Fuck you, man.

ANSWERS >

1. **48HRS**
   1982, USA
   Director: Walter Hill
   Cast: Nick Nolte, Eddie Murphy, Annette O'Toole
   Screenplay: Roger Spottiswoode, Walter Hill, Larry Gross
   Steven E. de Souza and Jeb Stuart

2. **BUTCH CASSIDY AND THE SUNDANCE KID**
   1969, USA
   Director: George Roy Hill
   Cast: Paul Newman, Robert Redford, Katharine Ross
   Screenplay: William Goldman

3. **GHOSTBUSTERS**
   1984, USA
   Director: Ivan Reitman
   Cast: Bill Murray, Dan Aykroyd, Harold Ramis
   Screenplay: Dan Aykroyd, Harold Ramis and Rick Moranis

4. **A CLOCKWORK ORANGE**
   1971, USA
   Director: Stanley Kubrick
   Cast: Malcolm McDowell, Patrick Magee, Adrienne Corri
   Screenplay: Stanley Kubrick
   Based on the book by Anthony Burgess

5. **THE BIRDS**
   1963, USA
   Director: Alfred Hitchcock
   Cast: Rod Taylor, Tippi Hedren, Jessica Tandy
   Screenplay: Daphne Du Maurier and Evan Hunter

6. **BEVERLY HILLS COP**
   1984, USA
   Director: Martin Brest
   Cast: Eddie Murphy, Judge Reinhold, John Ashton
   Screenplay: Danilo Bach and Daniel Petrie Jr.

1. -Back there, I could fly a gunship. I could drive a tank. I was in
    charge of million dollar equipment. Back here, I can't even hold
    a job washin cars.

2. -How odd that it should end this way for us, after so many
    stimulating encounters. I almost regret it. Where shall I find
    a new adversary so close to my own level?
    -Try the local sewer.

3. -If you were not a bride, I would kiss you goodbye.
    -If I were not a bride, there would be no goodbyes to be said.

4. -I still wish you had't done that, Hildy.
    -Done what?
    -Divorced me. It makes a man feel he's not wanted.

    His Girl Friday

5. -Send me postcards from exotic ports of call. Isn't that what
    you call them? Exotic ports of call?
    -YOU'RE exotic!

6. -Man who catch fly with chopstick accomplish anything.
    -Ever catch one?
    -Not yet.

1. **FIRST BLOOD**
   1982, USA
   Director: Ted Kotcheff
   Cast: Sylvester Stallone, Richard Crenna, Brian Dennehy
   Screenplay: Michael Kozoll, William Sackheim, Sylvester Stallone
   Based on the book by David Morrell

2. **RAIDERS OF THE LOST ARK**
   1981, USA
   Director: Steven Spielberg
   Cast: Harrison Ford, Karen Allen, Wolf Kahler
   Screenplay: George Lucas, Philip Kaufman and Lawrence Kasdan

3. **BEN-HUR**
   1959, USA
   Director: William Wyler
   Cast: Charlton Heston, Jack Hawkins, Stephen Boyd
   Screenplay: Karl Tunberg, Maxwell Anderson, Christopher Fry and
   Gore Vidal
   Based on the book by Lew Wallace

4. **HIS GIRL FRIDAY**
   1940, USA
   Director: Howard Hawks
   Cast: Cary Grant, Rosalind Russell, Ralph Bellamy
   Screenplay: Ben Hecht, Charles MacArthur and Charles Lederer

5. **NO WAY OUT**
   1987, USA
   Director: Roger Donaldson
   Cast: Kevin Costner, Gene Hackman, Sean Young
   Screenplay: Robert Garland
   Based on the book by Kenneth Fearing

6. **THE KARATE KID**
   1984, USA
   Director: John G Avildsen
   Cast: Ralph Macchio, Noriyuki Morita, Elisabeth Shue
   Screenplay: Robert Mark Kamen

1. -Excuse me. What is your name? I'm Bob Woodward,
   of the Washington Post.
   -Markham.
   -Markham. Mr. Markham, are you here in connection with
   the Watergate burglary?
   -I'm not here.

   All the President's Men

2. -If I die, I'm sorry for all the bad things I did to you. And if I
   live, I'm sorry for all the bad things I'm gonna do to you.

3. -Well, obviously, those three girls were just the wrong three girls.

4. -What do you play?
   -I used to play football in school.
   -I mean, what instrument?
   -I don't.
   -Then what are you doing here?
   -Well, I saw everyone else lining up so I thought
   you were selling drugs.

5. -And crawling on this planet's face, some insects... called the
   human race. Lost in time. And lost in space... and meaning.

6. -Cosmo, call me a cab.
   -OK, you're a cab.

1. **ALL THE PRESIDENTS MEN**
   1976, USA
   Director: Alan J Pakula
   Cast: Robert Redford, Dustin Hoffman, Jason Roberts
   Screenplay: William Goldman
   Based on the book by Carl Bernstein and Bob Woodward

2. **ALL THAT JAZZ**
   1979, USA
   Director: Bob Fosse
   Cast: Roy Schneider, Jessica Lange, Ann Reinking
   Screenplay: Robert Alan Aurthur and Bob Fosse

3. **CABARET**
   1972, USA
   Director: Bob Fosse
   Cast: Liza Minelli, Michael York, Helmut Griem
   Screenplay: John Van Druten, Joe Masteroff, Jay Presson Allen and Hugh Wheeler
   Based on the book by Christopher Isherwood

4. **THE COMMITMENTS**
   1991, UNITED KINGDOM
   Director: Alan Parker
   Cast: Robert Arkins, Michael Aherne, Angeline Ball
   Screenplay: Dick Clement, Ian La Frenais and Roddy Doyle
   Based on the book by Roddy Doyle

5. **THE ROCKY HORROR PICTURE SHOW**
   1975, USA
   Director: Jim Sharman
   Cast: Tim Curry, Susan Sarandon, Barry Bostwick
   Screenplay: Richard O'Brien, Jim Sharman

6. **SINGIN' IN THE RAIN**
   1952, USA
   Director: Gene Kelly, Stanley Donen
   Cast: Gene Kelly, Debbie Reynolds, Donald O'Connor
   Screenplay: Betty Comden and Adolph Green

1. Survival kit contents check. In them, you'll find: one .45 caliber automatic; two boxes of ammunition; four days concentrated emergency rations; one drug issue containing: antibiotics, morphine, vitamin pills, pep pills, sleeping pills, tranquilizer pills; one miniature combination Russian phrase book and bible; one hundred dollars in rubles; one hundred dollars in gold; nine packs of chewing gum; one issue of prophylactics; three lipsticks; three pair of nylon stockings. Shoot, a fellah could have a pretty good weekend in Vegas with all that stuff.

    Dr. Strangelove

2. -It looks like you will see Berlin before I do.

3. -Don't feel bad about losing your virtue. I sort of knew you would. Everybody always does.

4. -Have you any famous last words?
    -Not yet.
    -Not yet? Is that famous?

5. -Do you believe in God, Sargeant?
    -I believe God is a sadist, but probably doesn't even know it.

6. -You forgive me?
    -Nothing is forgiven. Nothing.

ANSWERS >

1. DR STRANGELOVE OR: HOW I LEARNED TO STOP
    WORRYING AND LOVE THE BOMB
    1963, UNITED KINGDOM
    Director: Stanley Kubrick
    Cast: Peter Sellers, George C Scott, Sterling Hayden
    Screenplay: Stanley Kubrick, Terry Southern and Peter George III
    Based on the book by Peter George

2. THE GREAT ESCAPE
    1962, USA
    Director: John Sturges,
    Cast: Steve McQueen, James Garner, Richard Attenborough
    Screenplay: James Clavell and W.R. Burnett
    Based on the book by Paul Brickhill

3. KLUTE
    1971, USA
    Director: Alan J Pakula
    Cast: Jane Fonda, Donald Sutherland, Charles Cioffi
    Screenplay: Andy Lewis and Dave Lewis

4. THE ADVENTURES OF BARON MUNCHAUSEN
    1989, UNITED KINGDOM
    Director: Terry Gilliam
    Cast: John Neville, Eric Idle, Sarah Polley
    Screenplay: Terry Gilliam and Charles McKeown
    Based on the book by Rudolph Erich Raspe

5. CROSS OF IRON
    1977, UNITED KINGDOM/WEST GERMANY
    Director: Sam Peckinpah
    Cast: James Coburn, Maximilian Schell, James Mason
    Screenplay: Julius J. Epstein, James Hamilton and Walter Kelley
    Based on the book by Frederick Forsyth

6. THE KILLING FIELDS
    1984, UNITED KINGDOM
    Director: Roland Joffe
    Cast: Sam Waterston, Haing S Ngor, John Malkovich
    Screenplay: Bruce Robinson

1. -Somewhere out there is the beast and he's hungry tonight.
   -Have you ever gotten into a mistake that you just can't
   get out of?
   -There is a way out of everything, man. Just keep your
   pecker hard and your powder dry and the world will turn.

2. -The army doesn't like more than one disaster in a day.
   -Looks bad in the newspapers and upsets civilians
   at their breakfast.

3. -I've killed women and children. I've killed everything that walks
   or crawls at one time or another. And I'm here to kill you, Little Bill,
   for what you done to Ned.

4. -What I like and what I need are two different things.

5. -Four dollars? You know what four dollars buys today?
   It don't even buy three dollars!

6. -Have you read the Bible, Pete?
   -Holy Bible?
   -Yeah.
   -Yeah, I think so. Anyway, I've heard about it.

1. **PLATOON**
    1986, USA
    Director: Oliver Stone
    Cast: Tom Berenger, Willem Dafoe, Charlie Sheen
    Screenplay: Oliver Stone

2. **ZULU**
    1963, UNITED KINGDOM
    Director: Cy Endfield
    Cast: Stanley Baker, Jack Hawkins, Ulla Jacobsson
    Screenplay: John Prebble, John Prebble and Cy Endfield

3. **UNFORGIVEN**
    1992, USA
    Director: Clint Eastwood
    Cast: Clint Eastwood, Gene Hackman, Morgan Freeman
    Screenplay: David Webb Peoples

4. **THE WILD BUNCH**
    1969, USA
    Director: Sam Peckinpah
    Cast: William Holden, Ernest Borgnine, Robert Ryan
    Screenplay: Walon Green, Roy N. Sickner, Walon Green and
    Sam Peckinpah

5. **SATURDAY NIGHT FEVER**
    1977, USA
    Director: John Badham
    Cast: John Travolta, Karen Lynn Gorney, Barry Miller
    Screenplay: Nik Cohn and Norman Wexler

6. **BARTON FINK**
    1991, USA
    Director: Joel Coen
    Cast: John Turturro, John Goodman, Judy Davis
    Screenplay: Ethan Coen and Joel Coen

1.   -Money is the world's curse.
    -May the Lord smite me with it! And may I never recover!

2.   -Then one day I hear Reach for it mister! I spun around,
    and there I was standing face to face with a six year old kid.
    Well, I just laid down my guns and walked away. Little bastard
    shot me in the ass!

3.   -You got a letter from headquarters this morning.
    -What is it?
    -It's a big building where generals meet, but that's not important.

4.   -We are the Knights who say... NI!

Monty Python and the Holy Grail

5.   -You know, I got a hunch, Fat Man. I got a hunch that it's me
    from here on in. One ball, corner pocket. I mean, that ever happen
    to you? You know, all of a sudden you feel like you just can't
    miss? 'Cause I dreamed about this game, fat man. I dreamed
    about it every night on the road. Five ball. You know, this is my
    table, man. I own it.

6.   -What do you want?
    -Oh, little song, little dance, Batman's head on a lance...

ANSWERS >

1. **FIDDLER ON THE ROOF**
   1971, USA
   Director: Norman Jewison
   Cast: Topol, Norma Crane, Leonard Frey
   Screenplay: Joseph Stein
   Based on the book by Sholom Aleichem

2. **BLAZING SADDLES**
   1973, USA
   Director: Mel Brooks
   Cast: Cleavon Little, Gene Wilder, Harvey Korman
   Screenplay: Andrew Bergman, Mel Brooks, Richard Pryor,
   Norman Steinberg and Alan Uger

3. **AIRPLANE! / FLYING HIGH**
   1980, USA
   Director: Jim Abrahams, David Zucker, Jerry Zucker
   Cast: Robert Hays, Julie Hagerty, Robert Stack
   Screenplay: Jim Abrahams, David Zucker and Jerry Zucker

4. **MONTY PYTHON AND THE HOLY GRAIL**
   1974, UNITED KINGDOM
   Director: Terry Gilliam, Terry Jones
   Cast: Graham Chapman, John Cleese, Terry Gilliam
   Screenplay: Graham Chapman, John Cleese, Eric Idle, Terry Gilliam,
   Terry Jones and Michael Palin

5. **THE HUSTLER**
   1961, USA
   Director: Robert Rossen
   Cast: Paul Newman, Jackie Gleason, Piper Lauire
   Screenplay: Sidney Carroll and Robert Rossen
   Based on the book by Walter Tevis

6. **BATMAN**
   1989, USA
   Director: Tim Burton
   Cast: Jack Nicholson, Michael Keaton, Kim Basinger
   Screenplay: Bob Kane, Sam Hamm and Warren Skaaren

1. -Your middle name is Ralph, as in puke, your birthdate's March 12th, you're 5'9 and a half, you weigh 130 pounds and your social security number is 049380913.
    -Wow! Are you psychic?
    -No.
    -Well, would you mind telling me how you know all this about me?
    -I stole your wallet.

2. -If you were happy every day of your life, you wouldn't be a human being. You'd be a game-show host.

3. -I'll send you a love letter! Straight from my heart, fucker! You know what a love letter is? It's a bullet from a fucking gun, fucker! You recieve a love letter from me, you're fucked forever! You understand, fuck? I'll send you straight to hell, fucker!

4. -A copper. A copper. How do you like that boys? A copper, and his name is Fallon. And we went for it. I went for it. Treated him like a kid brother. And I was gonna split fifty-fifty with a copper!

5. -I hope he likes spaghetti. They serve it four times a day in Italian prisons!

6. -Your car's uglier than I am. That didn't come out right.

ANSWERS >

1. THE BREAKFAST CLUB
   1985, USA
   Director: John Hughes
   Cast: Emilio Esteves, Judd Nelson, Molly Ringwald
   Screenplay: John Hughes

2. HEATHERS
   1989, USA
   Director: Michael Lehmann
   Cast: Winona Ryder, Christian Slater, Shannen Doherty
   Screenplay: Daniel Waters

3. BLUE VELVET
   1986, USA
   Director: David Lynch
   Cast: Kyle MacLachlan, Isabella Rossellini, Dennis Hopper
   Screenplay: David Lynch

4. WHITE HEAT
   1949, USA
   Director: Raoul Walsh
   Cast: James Cagney, Virginia Mayo, Edmond O'Brien
   Screenplay: Virginia Kellogg, Ivan Goff and Ben Roberts

5. THE ITALIAN JOB
   1969, UNITED KINGDOM
   Director: Peter Collinson
   Cast: Michael Caine, Noel Coward, Maggie Blye
   Screenplay: Troy Kennedy-Martin

6. AMERICAN GRAFFITI
   1973, USA
   Director: George Lucas
   Cast: Richard Dreyfuss, Ronny Howard, Paul LeMat
   Screenplay: George Lucas, Gloria Katz and Willard Huyck

1.　-Is drinking a way of killing yourself?
　　-Or, is killing myself a way of drinking?

2.　-All I know is that this violates every canon of respectable
　　broadcasting. We're not a respectable network. We're a
　　whorehouse network, and we have to take whatever we can get.

3.　-Hey, you wanna hear my philosophy of life? Do it to him
　　before he does it to you.

4.　-Our knowledge as made us cynical; our cleverness, hard
　　and unkind. We think too much and feel too little.

5.　-I'm gonna buy me a herd of chorus girls and make
　　'em dance on my bed.

6.　-This may seem like a really stupid question...
　　-There *are* no stupid questions.
　　-You inherit 5 million dollars the same day aliens land on the
　　earth and say they're going to blow it up in 2 days.
　　What do you do?
　　-That's the stupidest question I've ever heard.

1. LEAVING LAS VEGAS
   1995, USA
   Director: Mike Figgis
   Cast: Nicolas Cage, Elisabeth Shue, Julian Sands
   Screenplay: Mike Figgis
   Based on the book by John O'Brien

2. NETWORK
   1976, USA
   Director: Sidney Lumet
   Cast: William Holden, Faye Dunaway, Peter Finch
   Screenplay: Paddy Chayefsky

3. WATERFRONT
   1950 UNITED KINGDOM
   Director: Michael Anderson
   Cast: Robert Newton, Kathleen Harrison
   Screenplay: John Brophy, Paul Soskin

4. THE GREAT DICTATOR
   1940, USA
   Director: Charles Chaplin
   Cast: Charles Chaplin, Jack Oakie, Reginald Gardiner
   Screenplay: Charles Chaplin

5. JAILHOUSE ROCK
   1957, USA
   Director: Richard Thorpe
   Cast: Elvis Presley, Judy Tyler, Vaughn Taylor
   Screenplay: Nedrick Young and Guy Trosper

6. HEATHERS
   1989, USA
   Director: Michael Lehmann
   Cast: Winona Ryder, Christian Slater, Shannen Doherty
   Screenplay: Daniel Waters

1.   -They wanted in Hollywood to make the definitive spy picture. And they came to me to supervise the project, you know, because I think that, if you know me at all, you know that death is my bread and danger my butter - oh, no, danger's my bread, and death is my butter. No, no, wait. Danger's my bread, death no, death is - no, I'm sorry. Death is my - death and danger are my various breads and various butters.

2.   I don't remember yesterday. Today it rained.

3.   -Muhammad Ali, he was like a sleeping elephant. You can do whatever you want around a sleeping elephant; whatever you want. But when he wakes up, he tramples everything.

4.   -Don't cry at the beginning of a date. Cry at the end, like I do.

        Jerry Maguire

5.   -He says the sun came out last night. He says it sang to him.

6.   -Ay, fight and you may die. Run and you'll live. At least a while. And dying in your beds many years from now, would you be willing to trade all the days from this day to that for one chance, just one chance, to come back here and tell our enemies that they may take our lives, but they'll never take our freedom?

ANSWERS >

1.   WHAT'S UP TIGER LILY?
        1966, JAPAN
        Director: Senkichi Taniguchi
        Cast: Tatsuya Mihashi, Miya Hana, Eiko Wakabayashi
        Screenplay: Woody Allen, Julie Bennett, Frank Buxton, Louise Lasser,
        Len Maxwell, Mickey Rose and Bryan Wilson

2.   THREE DAYS OF THE CONDOR
        1975, USA
        Director: Sydney Pollack
        Cast: Robert Redford, Faye Dunaway, Cliff Robertson
        Screenplay: Lorenzo Semple Jr and David Rayfiel
        Based on the book by James Grady

3.   WHEN WE WERE KINGS
        1996, USA
        Director: Leon Gast
        Cast: Muhammad Ali, George Forman, Don King

4.   JERRY MAGUIRE
        USA
        Director: Cameron Crowe
        Cast: Tom Cruise, Cuba Gooding Jr, Renee Zellweger
        Screenplay: Cameron Crowe

5.   CLOSE ENCOUNTERS OF THE THIRD KIND
        1977, USA
        Director: Steven Spielberg
        Cast: Richard Dreyfuss, Francois Truffaut, Teri Garr
        Screenplay: Steven Spielberg, Hal Barwood, Jerry Belson, John Hill
        and Matthew Robbins.

6.   BRAVEHEART
        1995, USA
        Director: Mel Gibson
        Cast: Mel Gibson, Sophie Marceau, Patrick McGoohan
        Screenplay: Randall Wallace

1. -I don't feel the sickness yet, but it's in the post. That's for sure.
    I'm in the junkie limbo at the moment. Too ill to sleep. Too tired to
    stay awake, but the sickness is on its way. Sweat, chills, nausea.
    Pain and craving. A need like nothing else I've ever known will
    soon take hold of me. It's on its way.

2. -Even a stopped clock tells the right time twice a day, and
    for once I'm inclined to believe Withnail is right. We are indeed
    drifting into the arena of the unwell.

3. -May I please see your license?
    -Huh?
    -Your license. May I please see your license?
    -Hey, man, ain't it up there on the bumper, man?

4. -He who draws the sword from the stone, he shall be king.
    Arthur, you're the one!

    Excalibur

5. -How did you know? How did you know I'd respond
    to you the way I have?
    -I saw myself in you.

6. -If anything in this life is certain, if history has taught
    us anything, it is that you can kill anyone.

1. TRAINSPOTTING
    1996, UNITED KINGDOM
    Director: Danny Boyle
    Cast: Ewan McGregor, Ewan Bremmer, Jonny Lee Miller
    Screenplay: John Hodge
    Based on the book by Irvine Welsh

2. WITHNAIL AND I
    1986, UNITED KINGDOM
    Director: Bruce Robinson
    Cast: Richard E Grant, Paul McGann, Richard Griffiths
    Screenplay: Bruce Robinson

3. UP IN SMOKE
    1978, USA
    Director: Lou Adler
    Cast: Cheech Marin, Tommy Chong, Stacy Keach
    Screenplay: Tommy Chong and Cheech Marin

4. EXCALIBUR
    1981, UNITED KINGDOM
    Director: John Boorman
    Cast: Nicol Williamson, Nigel Terry, Helen Mirren
    Screenplay: Rospo Pallenberg and John Boorman
    Based on the book by Thomas Malory

5. NINE 1/2 WEEKS
    1986, USA
    Director: Adrian Lyne
    Cast: Mickey Rourke, Kim Basinger, Margaret Whitton
    Screenplay: Sarah Kernandan, Zalman King, Patricia Louisianna Knop
    Based on the book by Elizabeth McNeill

6. THE GODFATHER PART II
    1974, USA
    Director: Francis Ford Coppola
    Cast: Al Pacino, Robert De Niro, Robert Duvall,
    Screenplay: Mario Puzo and Francis Ford Coppola

1. -You know, we always called each other goodfellas. Like, you'd say to somebody: You're gonna like this guy; he's all right. He's a goodfella. He's one of us. You understand? We were goodfellas, wiseguys.

Goodfellas

2. -You see, I have a story too, Mr. Bailey. I had a friend once. A dear friend. I turned him in to save his life. He died. But he wanted it that way. Things went bad for my friend, and they went bad for me too.

3. -You wanna fuck with me? Okay. You wanna play rough? Okay. Say hello to my little friend.

4. -Are you afraid to die, Spartacus?
   -No more than I was to be born.

Spartacus

5. -Well, Denham, the airplanes got him.
   -Oh, no. It wasn't the airplanes. It was beauty that killed the beast.

6. -Ray, people will come, Ray. They'll come to Iowa for reasons they can't even fathom. They'll turn up your driveway, not knowing for sure why they're doing it. They'll arrive at your door as innocent as children, longing for the past.

ANSWERS >

1.   **GOODFELLAS**
     1990, USA
     Director: Martin Scorsese
     Cast: Robert De Niro, Ray Liotta, Joe Pesci
     Screenplay: Nicholas Pileggi and Martin Scorsese
     Based on the book by Nicholas Pileggi

2.   **ONCE UPON A TIME IN AMERICA**
     1984, USA
     Director: Sergio Leone
     Cast: Robert De Niro, James Woods, Elizabeth McGovern
     Screenplay: Leonardo Benvenuti, Piero De Bernardi, Enrico Medioli,
     Franco Arcalli, Franco Ferrini, Sergio Leone, Stuart Kaminsky and
     Ernesto Gastaldi
     Based on the book by Harry Grey

3.   **SCARFACE**
     1983, USA
     Director: Brian De Palma
     Cast: Al Pacino, Steven Bauer, Michelle Pfeiffer
     Screenplay: Oliver Stone and Howard Hawks
     Based on the book by Armitage Trail

4.   **SPARTACUS**
     1960, USA
     Director: Stanley Kubrick
     Cast: Kirk Douglas, Laurence Olivier, Jean Simmons
     Screenplay: Dalton Trumbo, Calder Willingham and Peter Ustinov
     Based on the book by Howard Fast

5.   **KING KONG**
     1976, USA
     Director: John Guillermin
     Cast: Jeff Bridges, Charles Grodin, Jessica Lange
     Screenplay: Merian C. Cooper, Edgar Wallace, James Ashmore
     Creelman, Ruth Rose and Lorenzo Semple Jr.

6.   **FIELD OF DREAMS**
     1989, USA
     Director: Phil Alden Robinson
     Cast: Kevin Costner, Amy Madigan, Gaby Hoffman
     Screenplay: Phil Alden Robinson
     Based on the book W.P. Kinsella

1. -I hope they don't hang you, Precious, by that sweet neck.
    The chances are you'll get off with life. That means if you're a
    good girl, you'll be out in 20 years. I'll be waiting for you. If they
    hang you...I'll always remember you.

2. -Inside the Ark are treasures beyond your wildest aspirations.
    You want to see it opened as well as I. Indiana, we are simply
    passing through history. This, this *is* history.

    Raiders of the Lost Ark

3. -I'm tired, I've been drinking since nine o'clock. My wife is
    vomiting. There's been a lot of screaming going on around here!

4. -We were attracted to each other at the party. That was obvious!
    You're on your own for the night, that's also obvious...
    We're two adults.

5. -This was no boat accident. It was no boat propeller. It wasn't
    any coral reef, and it wasn't Jack the Ripper. It was a shark.

    Jaws

6. -DO YOU SEE THE LIGHT?!!
    -What light?!
    -DO YOU SEEEE THE LIGHT?!
    -YES!! YES!! JESUS H. TAP-DANCING CHRIST...I HAVE
    SEEN THE LIGHT!!!

ANSWERS >

1. **THE MALTESE FALCON**
   1941, USA
   Director: John Huston
   Cast: Humphrey Bogart, Mary Astor, Peter Lorre
   Screenplay: John Huston
   Based on the book by Dashell Hammett

2. **RAIDERS OF THE LOST ARK**
   1981, USA
   Director: Steven Spielberg
   Cast: Harrison Ford, Karen Allen, Wolf Kahler
   Screenplay: George Lucas, Philip Kaufman and Lawrence Kasdan

3. **WHO'S AFRAID OF VIRGINIA WOOLF**
   1966, USA
   Director: Mike Nichols
   Cast: Elizabeth Taylor, Richard Burton, George Segal
   Screenplay: Edward Albee and Ernest Lehman

4. **FATAL ATTRACTION**
   1987, USA
   Director: Adrian Lyne
   Cast: Michael Douglas, Glenn Close, Anne Archer
   Screenplay: James Dearden and Nicholas Meyer

5. **JAWS**
   1975, USA
   Director: Steven Spielberg
   Cast: Roy Scheider, Robert Shaw, Richard Dreyfuss
   Screenplay: Peter Benchley, Carl Gottlieb, John Milius, Howard
   Sackler and Robert Shaw
   Based on the book by Peter Benchley

6. **THE BLUES BROTHERS**
   1980, USA
   Director: John Landis
   Cast: John Belushi, Dan Aykroyd, Cap Calloway
   Screenplay: Dan Aykroyd and John Landis

1. -You see a girl a couple of times a week and sooner or later,
   she thinks you'll divorce your wife. Not fair, is it?
   -No. Especially to your wife.

2. -Crucifixion?
   -Yes.
   -Good. Out of the door, line on the left, one cross each.
   -Crucifixion?
   -Er, no. Freedom, actually.
   -What?
   -Yeah, they said I hadn't done anything and I could go
   and live on an island somewhere.
   -Oh, I say! That's very nice. Well, off you go then.
   -No, I'm just pulling your leg, it's crucifixion really.
   -Oh yes, very good. Well...
   -Yes, I know. Out of the door, one cross each, line on the left.

   Monty Python's Life of Brian

3. -You see, Mr. Scott? In the water, I'm a very skinny lady!

4. -You know those days when you get the mean reds?

5. -Flowers are simply tarts; prostitutes for the bees.

6. -Where ya from, man?
   -Hard to say.

ANSWERS >

1.   THE APARTMENT
      1960, USA
      Director: Billy Wilder
      Cast: Jack Lemmon, Shirley MacLaine, Fred MacMurray
      Screenplay: Billy Wilder and I.A.L. Diamond

2.   MONTY PYTHON'S LIFE OF BRIAN
      1979, UNITED KINGDOM
      Director: Terry Jones
      Cast: Graham Chapman, John Cleese, Terry Gilliam
      Screenplay: Graham Chapman, John Cleese, Terry Gilliam, Eric Idle,
      Terry Jones and Michael Palin

3.   THE POSEIDON ADVENTURE
      1972, USA
      Director: Ronald Neame
      Cast: Gene Hackman, Ernest Borgnine, Red Buttons
      Screenplay: Wendell Mayes and Stirling Silliphant
      Based on the book by Paul Gallico

4.   BREAKFAST AT TIFFANY'S
      1961, USA
      Director: Blake Edwards
      Cast: Audrey Hepburn, George Peppard
      Screenplay: Truman Capote, George Axelrod

5.   WITHNAIL AND I
      1986, UNITED KINGDOM
      Director: Bruce Robinson
      Cast: Richard E Grant, Paul McGann, Richard Griffiths
      Screenplay: Bruce Robinson

6.   EASY RIDER
      1969, USA
      Director: Dennis Hopper
      Cast: Peter Fonda, Dennis Hopper, Jack Nicholson
      Screenplay: Peter Fonda, Dennis Hopper and Terry Southern

1. -Jesus, Bob. You never told us anything about not mentioning dogs.
    -The reason nobody mentioned dogs, Rick, is that to mention the dog would have been a hex in itself.
    -All right. Well, now we are on the subject, are there an other stupid things we aren't supposed to mention that will affect our future?

2. -Lower your flags, and march straight back to England, stopping at every home to beg forgiveness for a hundred years of theft, rape, and murder. Do this, and your men shall live. Do it not, and every one of you will die today.

    Braveheart

3. -It happens sometimes. People just explode. Natural causes.

4. -You know, I'd almost forgotten what your eyes looked like. Still the same. Pissholes in the snow.

5. -You can get further with a kind word and a gun than you can with just a kind word.

6. -It's when you start doing things for free, that you start to grow wings. Isn't that right, Mike?
    -What?
    -Wings, Michael. You grow wings, and become a fairy.

ANSWERS >

1. DRUGSTORE COWBOY
   1989, USA
   Director: Gus Van Sant
   Cast: Matt Dillon, Kelly Lynch, James Remar
   Screenplay: Gus Van Sant, Daniel Yost and William S. Burroughs
   Based on the book by James Fogle

2. BRAVEHEART
   1995, USA
   Director: Mel Gibson
   Cast: Mel Gibson, Sophie Marceau, Patrick McGoohan
   Screenplay: Randall Wallace

3. REPO MAN
   1984, USA
   Director: Alex Cox
   Cast: Emilio Estevez, Harry Dean Stanton, Vonetta McGee
   Screenplay: Alex Cox

4. GET CARTER
   1971, UNITED KINGDOM
   Director: Mike Hodges
   Cast: Michael Caine, Ian Hendry, Britt Ekland
   Screenplay: Mike Hodges
   Based on the book by Ted Lewis

5. THE UNTOUCHABLES
   1987, USA
   Director: Brian De Palma
   Cast: Kevin Costner, Sean Connery, Charles Martin Smith
   Screenplay: David Mamet
   Based on the book by Oscar Fraley and Eliot Ness and Paul Robsky

6. MY OWN PRIVATE IDAHO
   1991, USA
   Director: Gus Van Sant
   Cast: River Phoenix, Keanu Reeves, James Russo
   Screenplay: Gus Van Sant

1. -Do you feel that playing rock 'n' roll music keeps you a child?
   That is, keeps you in a state of arrested development?
   -No. No. No. I feel it's like, it's more like going, going to a, a
   national park or something. And there's, you know, they preserve
   the moose. And that's, that's my childhood up there on stage.
   That moose, you know.
   -So when you're playing you feel like a preserved moose
   on stage?
   -Yeah.

2. -Have you been following that man?
   -Yeah, I've been following him on my own time.
   And anybody can tell I didn't do that to him.
   -How?
   -Cause he looks too damn good, that's how!

3. -Six days does not a week make.

4. -You're not very bright, are you? I like that in a man.

5. -It's important to think. It's what separates us from lentils.

6. -Paulie might have moved slow, but it was only because
   Paulie didn't have to move for anybody.

ANSWERS >

1.   **THIS IS SPINAL TAP**
   1984, USA
   Director: Rob Reiner
   Cast: Michael McKean, Christopher Guest, Harry Shearer
   Screenplay: Christopher Guest, Michael McKean, Rob Reiner and
   Harry Shearer

2.   **DIRTY HARRY**
   1971, USA
   Director: Don Siegal
   Cast: Clint Eastwood, Harry Guardino, Reni Santoni
   Screenplay: Harry Julian Fink, Rita M. Fink, Dean Riesner and
   John Milius

3.   **BAREFOOT IN THE PARK**
   1967, USA
   Director: Gene Saks
   Cast: Robert Redford, Jane Fonda, Charles Boyer
   Screenplay: Neil Simon

4.   **BODY HEAT**
   1981, USA
   Director: Lawrence Kasdan
   Cast: William Hurt, Kathleen Turner, Richard Crenna
   Screenplay: Lawrence Kasdan

5.   **THE FISHER KING**
   1991, USA
   Director: Terry Gilliam
   Cast: Robin Williams, Jeff Bridges, Amanda Plummer
   Screenplay: Richard LaGravenese

6.   **GOODFELLAS**
   1990, USA
   Director: Martin Scorsese
   Cast: Robert De Niro, Ray Liotta, Joe Pesci
   Screenplay: Nicholas Pileggi and Martin Scorsese
   Based on the book by Nicholas Pileggi

1.　-It has been established that persons who have recently died have been returning to life and committing acts of murder.

2.　-We're here to meet a friend. Comin' on the train.
　　-Nothin' comin' on the train except a couple of crates and a... uh... coffin!
　　-Our friend.

3.　-Last night, Darth Vader came down from planet Vulcan and told me that if I didn't take Lorraine out that he'd melt my brain.

Back to the Future

4.　-Nicky's methods of betting weren't scientific, but they worked. When he won, he collected. When he lost, he told the bookies to go fuck themselves. I mean, what were they going to do, muscle Nicky? Nicky was the muscle.

5.　-I must be crazy to be in a loony bin like this.

One Flew over the Cuckoo's Nest

6.　-I done something new for this fight! I done rassled with a alligator! That's right, I have rassled with a alligator. I done tussled with a whale! I done handcuffed lightning, throwed thunder in jail! That's bad. Only last week, I murdered a rock, injured a stone, hospitalized a brick. I'm so mean, I make medicine sick!

ANSWERS >

1.   NIGHT OF THE LIVING DEAD
     1968, USA
     Director: George A Romero
     Cast: Duane Jones, Judith O'Dea, Russell Streiner
     Screenplay: George A. Romero and John A. Russo

2.   MAD MAX
     1979, AUSTRALIA
     Director: George Miller
     Cast: Mel Gibson, Joanne Samuel, Hugh Keays Byrne
     Screenplay: James McCausland and George Miller

3.   BACK TO THE FUTURE
     1985, USA
     Director: Robert Zemeckis
     Cast: Michael J Fox, Christopher Lloyd, Crispin Glover
     Screenplay: Robert Zemeckis and Bob Gale

4.   CASINO
     1995, USA
     Director: Martin Scorsese
     Cast: Robert De Niro, Sharon Stone Joe Pesci
     Screenplay: Nicholas Pileggi and Martin Scorsese
     Based on the book by Nicholas Pileggi

5.   ONE FLEW OVER THE CUCKOO'S NEST
     1975, USA
     Director: Milos Forman
     Cast: Jack Nicholson, Louise Fletcher, Brad Dourif
     Screenplay. Bo Goldman and Lawrence Hauben
     Based on the book by Ken Kesey

6.   WHEN WE WERE KINGS
     1996, USA
     Director: Leon Gast
     Cast: Muhammad Ali, George Forman, Don King

1. -D'you know that the human head weighs 8 pounds?
    -Did you know that Troy Aikman, in only six years, has passed for 16,303 yards?
    -D'you know that bees and dogs can smell fear?
    -Did you know that the career record for hits is 4,256 by Pete Rose who is NOT in the Hall of Fame?
    -D'you know that my next door neighbor has three rabbits?
    -I... I can't compete with that!

    Jerry Maguire

2. -I don't think I want to know you very well. I don't think you're gonna live much longer.

3. -All right, men. We're on water. I don't want any of you walking to far to the left, or to the right. Remember the training films we saw about how people sink?

4. -Tell me something, my friend. You ever dance with the devil by the pale moonlight?

5. -She asks me why I'm such a hairy guy.

6. -Now come on, fellas. You wouldn't hit a bloke with no trousers on would you?
    -Alright, Charlie, put your trousers on.

ANSWERS >

1.   **JERRY MAGUIRE**
       1996, USA
       Director: Cameron Crowe
       Cast: Tom Cruise, Cuba Gooding Jr, Renee Zellweger
       Screenplay: Cameron Crowe

2.   **THREE DAYS OF THE CONDOR**
       1975, USA
       Director: Sydney Pollack
       Cast: Robert Redford, Faye Dunaway, Cliff Robertson
       Screenplay: Lorenzo Semple Jr and David Rayfiel
       Based on the book by James Grady

3.   **WHAT'S UP TIGER LILY?**
       1966, JAPAN
       Director: Senkichi Taniguchi
       Cast: Tatsuya Mihashi, Miya Hana, Eiko Wakabayashi
       Screenplay: Woody Allen, Julie Bennett, Frank Buxton, Louise Lasser,
       Len Maxwell, Mickey Rose and Bryan Wilson

4.   **BATMAN**
       1989, USA
       Director: Tim Burton
       Cast: Jack Nicholson, Michael Keaton, Kim Basinger
       Screenplay: Bob Kane, Sam Hamm and Warren Skaaren

5.   **HAIR**
       1979, USA
       Director: Milos Forman
       Cast: John Savage, Treat Williams, Beverly D'Angelo
       Screenplay: Gerome Ragni, James Rado, Galt MacDermot and
       Michael Weller

6.   **THE ITALIAN JOB**
       1969, UNITED KINGDOM
       Director: Peter Collinson
       Cast: Michael Caine, Noel Coward, Maggie Blye
       Screenplay: Troy Kennedy-Martin

1. -The soul of man has been given wings and at last he is
   beginning to fly. He is flying into the rainbow! Into the light
   of hope!

2. -Morning, Lapoody.
   -Morning, Reverend.

3. -Impressive. Most impressive. Obi-wan has taught you well.
   You have controlled your fear. Now, release your anger! Only
   your hatred can destroy me!

   Empire Strikes Back

4. -I've got a job, a secretary, a mother, two ex-wives and several
   bartenders dependent upon me, and I don't intend to disappoint
   them all by getting myself slightly killed.

5. -What happened to your nose, Gittes? Somebody slammed
   a bedroom window on it?
   -Nope. Your wife got excited. She crossed her legs a little too
   quick. You understand what I mean, pal?

6. -J.W., this fellow's from England, see, and he's over here
   workin' with our government, sort of a... secret agent.
   -Secret Agent? On whose side?

141

ANSWERS >

1. THE GREAT DICTATOR
   1940, USA
   Director: Charles Chaplin
   Cast: Charles Chaplin, Jack Oakie, Reginald Gardiner
   Screenplay: Charles Chaplin

2. THE GODS MUST BE CRAZY
   1980, BOTSWANA
   Director: Jamie Uys
   Cast: Marius Weyers, Sandra Prinsloo, N!xau
   Screenplay: Jamie Uys

3. THE EMPIRE STRIKES BACK
   1980, USA
   Director: Irwin Kershner
   Cast: Mark Hamill, Harrison Ford, Carrie Fisher
   Screenplay: George Lucas, Leigh Brackett and Lawrence Kasdan

4. NORTH BY NORTHWEST
   1959, USA
   Director: Alfred Hitchcock
   Cast: Cary Grant, Eva Marie Saint, James Mason
   Screenplay: Ernest Lehman

5. CHINATOWN
   1974, USA
   Director: Roman Polanski
   Cast: Jack Nicholson, Faye Dunaway, John Huston
   Screenplay: Robert Towne and Roman Polanski

6. LIVE AND LET DIE
   1973, UNITED KINGDOM
   Director: Guy Hamilton
   Cast: Roger Moore, Yaphet Kotto, Jane Seymour
   Screenplay: Tom Mankiewicz.
   Based on the book by Ian Fleming

1.　-Hey, Bart. It's just me - Charlie
　　-Really? I hear it's Munt. Madman Munt.
　　-Geez. People can be so cruel. If it's not my build, it's
　　my personality.

2.　-A census taker once tried to test me. I ate his liver with some
　　fava beans and a nice Chianti.

　　Silence of the Lambs

3.　-You make it with some of these chicks, they think you gotta
　　dance with them.

4.　-Well, I guess he had it comin'.
　　-We all got it comin' kid.

5.　-There's something I've been meaning to ask you for some
　　time now.
　　-What's that?
　　-Can you cure me?
　　-No. We can care for you, but we can't cure you.

6.　-I find it difficult to convince myself that God would have
　　introduced such a foul being into creation without endowing
　　her with some virtues, hmmm?

ANSWERS >

1. **BARTON FINK**
   1991, USA
   Director: Joel Coen
   Cast: John Turturro, John Goodman, Judy Davis
   Screenplay: Ethan Coen and Joel Coen

2. **THE SILENCE OF THE LAMBS**
   1991, USA
   Director: Jonathan Demme
   Cast: Jodie Foster, Anthony Hopkins, Scott Glenn
   Screenplay: Ted Tally
   Based on the book by Thomas Harris

3. **SATURDAY NIGHT FEVER**
   1977, USA
   Director: John Badham
   Cast: John Travolta, Karen Lynn Gorney, Barry Miller
   Screenplay: Nik Cohn and Norman Wexler

4. **UNFORGIVEN**
   1992, USA
   Director: Clint Eastwood
   Cast: Clint Eastwood, Gene Hackman, Morgan Freeman
   Screenplay: David Webb Peoples

5. **THE ELEPHANT MAN**
   1980, USA
   Director: David Lynch
   Cast: Anthony Hopkins, John Hurt, Anne Bancroft
   Screenplay: Christopher De Vore, Eric Bergren and David Lynch
   Based on the book by Sir Frederick Treves and Ashley Montagu

6. **THE NAME OF THE ROSE**
   1986, FRANCE/ITALY/WEST-GERMANY
   Director: Jean Jacques Annaud
   Cast: Sean Connery, F Murray Abraham, Christian Slater
   Screenplay: Andrew Birkin, Gérard Brach, Howard Franklin and
   Alain Godard
   Based on the book by Umberto Eco

1. -Hold on to yourself, Bartlett. You're twenty feet short.
   -What do you mean, twenty feet short?
   -You're twenty feet short of the woods. The hole is right here out in open. The guard is between us and the lights.

2. -When I get out, you're dead!
   -You might be dead before you get out.

3. -Long people have short faces. Short people have long faces. Big people have little humor, and little people have no humor at all.

4. -I thrill when I drill a bicuspid / It's swell though they tell me I'm mal-ad-just-ed.

5. -When it comes to the safety of these people, there's me and then there's God, understand?

6. -Wait a minute, Doc. Ah... Are you telling me you built a time machine... out of a DeLorean?
   -The way I see it, if you're gonna build a time machine into a car, why not do it with some style?

   Back to the Future

ANSWERS >

1. THE GREAT ESCAPE
    1962, USA
    Director: John Sturges,
    Cast: Steve McQueen, James Garner, Richard Attenborough
    Screenplay: James Clavell and W.R. Burnett
    Based on the book by Paul Brickhill

2. ESCAPE FROM ALCATRAZ
    1979, USA
    Director: Donald Siegel
    Cast: Clint Eastwood, Patrick McGoohan, Roberts Blossom
    Screenplay: Richard Tuggle
    Based on the book by J. Campbell Bruce

3. SINGIN' IN THE RAIN
    1952, USA
    Director: Gene Kelly, Stanley Donen
    Cast: Gene Kelly, Debbie Reynolds, Donald O'Connor
    Screenplay: Betty Comden and Adolph Green

4. LITTLE SHOP OF HORRORS
    1986, USA
    Director: Frank Oz
    Cast: Rick Moranis, Ellen Greene, Vincent Gardenia
    Screenplay: Charles B. Griffith and Howard Ashman

5. THE ABYSS
    1989, USA
    Director: James Cameron
    Cast: Ed Harris, Mary Elizabeth Mastrantonio, Michael Biehn
    Screenplay: James Cameron

6. BACK TO THE FUTURE
    1985, USA
    Director: Robert Zemeckis
    Cast: Michael J Fox, Christopher Lloyd, Crispin Glover
    Screenplay: Robert Zemeckis and Bob Gale

1. -Why have you disturbed our sleep? Awakened us from our ancient slumber? YOU WILL DIE!!

2. -You know what you done there? You told my story. You told my whole story right there, right there. One time, I told you I was gonna make you somebody. That's what you done for me. You made me somebody they're gonna remember.

3. -Any time you try a decent crime, you got fifty ways you can fuck up. You think of twenty-five of them and you're a genius. And you ain't no genius. You remember who told me that?

4. -Ollie, you know my feelings about arming morons: you arm one, you've got to arm them all, otherwise it wouldn't be good sport.

5. -I move around a lot. Not because I'm looking for anything really, but 'cause I'm getting away from things that get bad if I stay.

6. -I run my unit how I run my unit. You want to investigate me? Roll the dice and take your chances. I eat breakfast 300 yards from 4000 Cubans who are trained to kill me, so don't think for one second that you can come down here, flash a badge, and make me nervous.

A Few Good Men

ANSWERS >

1.   **THE EVIL DEAD**
       1983, USA
       Director: Sam Raimi
       Cast: Bruce Campbell, Ellen Sandweiss, Hal Delrich
       Screenplay: Sam Raimii

2.   **BONNIE AND CLYDE**
       1967, USA
       Director: Arthur Penn
       Cast: Warren Beatty, Faye Dunaway, Michael J Pollard
       Screenplay: David Newman (III), Robert Benton and Robert Towne

3.   **BODY HEAT**
       1981, USA
       Director: Lawrence Kasdan
       Cast: William Hurt, Kathleen Turner, Richard Crenna
       Screenplay: Lawrence Kasdan

4.   **NOBODY'S FOOL**
       1994, USA
       Director: Robert Benton
       Cast: Paul Newman, Jessica Tandy, Bruce Willis
       Screenplay: Robert Benton
       Based on the book by Richard Russo

5.   **FIVE EASY PIECES**
       1970, USA
       Director: Bob Rafelson
       Cast: Jack Nicholson, Karen Black, Billy Green
       Screenplay: Carole Eastman and Bob Rafelson

6.   **A FEW GOOD MEN**
       1992, USA
       Director: Rob Reiner
       Cast: Tom Cruise, Jack Nicholson, Demi Moore
       Screenplay: Aaron Sorkin

1. -I remember when my daddy gave me that gun. He told me that I should never point it at anything in the house. And that he'd rather I'd shoot at tin cans in the backyard, but he said that sooner or later he supposed the temptation to go after birds would be too much, and that I could shoot all the blue jays I wanted, if I could hit 'em, but to remember it was a sin to kill a mockingbird. Well, I reckon because mockingbirds don't do anything but make music for us to enjoy.

    To kill a Mockingbird

2. - Never trust a nigger.
    - He could have been white.
    - Never trust anybody.

3. -I thought I knew you. But I'm not so sure anymore... Do you let anything reach you? I mean, really reach you?

4. -I saw Alan this morning and I keep wondering...
    -Alan's in Utah
    - ... And I keep wandering what I was doing in Utah.

5. -What I can't understand is how you can hit someone six times by accident.

6. -What are some of your favorite things to do?
    -Well, on Sundays I used to like to go hiking, but now...

ANSWERS >

1.   **TO KILL A MOCKINGBIRD**
      1962, USA
      Director: Robert Mulligan
      Cast: Gregory Peck, Mary Badham, Philip Alford
      Screenplay: Horton Foote
      Based on the book by Harper Lee

2.   **THE FRENCH CONNECTION**
      1971, USA
      Director: William Friedkin
      Cast: Gene Hackman, Fernando Rey, Roy Scheider
      Screenplay: Ernest Tidyman, Edward M. Keyes
      Based on the book by Robin Moore

3.   **BULLITT**
      1968, USA
      Director: Peter Yates
      Cast: Steve Mcqueen, Robert Vaughn, Jacqueline Bisset
      Screenplay: Alan Trustman and Harry Kleiner
      Based on the book by Robert L. Pike

4.   **FLETCH**
      1985, USA
      Director: Michael Ritchie
      Cast: Chevy Chase, Dana Wheeler Nicholson, Tim Matheson
      Screenplay: Andrew Bergman
      Based on the book by Gregory McDonald

5.   **FRIED GREEN TOMATOES**
      1991, USA
      Director: Jon Avnet
      Cast: Kathy Bates, Jessica Tandy, Mary Stuart Masterson
      Screenplay: Carol Sobieski, Fannie Flagg
      Based on the book by Fannie Flagg

6.   **THE BLAIR WITCH PROJECT**
      1999, USA
      Director: Daniel Myrick, Eduardo Sánchez
      Cast: Heather Donahue, Joshua Leonard, Michael C. Williams
      Screenplay: Daniel Myrick, Eduardo Sánchez

1. -Splendid, I thought. What did you think?
   -I, thought, splendid! What did you think?
   -Splendid, I thought.

2. -You still don't know what you're dealing with, do you?
   Perfect organism. Its structural perfection is matched
   only by its hostility.

3. -If I ever lay my two eyes on you again, I'm gonna walk right
   up to you and hammer on that monkeyed skull of yours 'til it
   rings like a Chinese gong!

   His Girl Friday

4. In the year of our Lord thirteen fourteen, patriots of Scotland,
   starving and outnumbered, charged the fields of Bannockburn.
   They fought like warrior poets. They fought like Scotsmen.
   And won their freedom.

   Braveheart

5. -As far back as I can remember, I always wanted
   to be a gangster.

6. -Truman, I've watched you your whole life. I saw you take your
   first step, your first word, your first kiss. I know you better than
   you know yourself. You're not going to walk out that door...
   -You never had a camera in my head.

ANSWERS >

1. **FOUR WEDDINGS AND A FUNERAL**
   1994, UNITED KINGDOM
   Director: Mike Newell
   Cast: Hugh Grant, Andie MacDowell, Kristin Scott Thomas
   Screenplay: Richard Curtis

2. **ALIEN**
   1979, USA
   Director: Ridley Scott
   Cast: Tom Skerritt, Sigourney Weaver, John Hurt
   Screenplay: Dan O'Bannon, Ronald Shusett, Dan O'Bannon, David Giler and Walter Hill

3. **HIS GIRL FRIDAY**
   1940, USA
   Director: Howard Hawks
   Cast: Cary Grant, Rosalind Russell, Ralph Bellamy
   Screenplay: Ben Hecht, Charles MacArthur and Charles Lederer

4. **BRAVEHEART**
   1995, USA
   Director: Mel Gibson
   Cast: Mel Gibson, Sophie Marceau, Patrick McGoohan
   Screenplay: Randall Wallace

5. **GOODFELLAS**
   1990, USA
   Director: Martin Scorsese
   Cast: Robert De Niro, Ray Liotta, Joe Pesci
   Screenplay: Nicholas Pileggi and Martin Scorsese
   Based on the book by Nicholas Pileggi

6. **THE TRUMAN SHOW**
   1998, USA
   Director: Peter Weir
   Cast: Jim Carrey, Laura Linney, Ed Harris
   Screenplay: Andrew Niccol

1.   -Well it's not a train. It's a prison word for... escape.
    But it doesn't stop around here.

2.   -Well, what are you going to do now? Shoot me?
    -No, I don't think so.
    -Then you're going to take these from me? If I could say a
    word about that...
    -No, you can keep them. You can keep as many as you can
    swallow.

3.   -Thank God for the rain, to wash the trash off the sidewalk.

4.   -Ya smoke this shit to escape from reality? Me, I don't
    need this shit. I am reality. There's the way it ought to be,
    and there's the way it is.

5.   -The life of the mind. There's no road map for that territory.
    Exploring it can be painful. I have a pain most people don't
    know anything about.

6.   -Protecting the Queen's safety is a task that is gladly accepted
    by Police Squad. No matter how silly the idea of having a queen
    might be to us, as Americans we must be gracious and
    considerate hosts.

ANSWERS >

1.   MIDNIGHT EXPRESS
      1978, UNITED KINGDOM
      Director: Alan Parker
      Cast: Brad Davis, Irene Miracle, Bo Hopkins
      Screenplay: Oliver Stone
      Based on the book by Billy Hayes and William Hoffer

2.   MARATHON MAN
      1976, USA
      Director: John Schlesinger
      Cast: Dustin Hoffman, Laurence Olivier, Roy Scheider
      Screenplay: Robert Towne and William Goldman
      Based on the book by William Goldman

3.   TAXI DRIVER
      1976, USA
      Director: Martin Scorsese
      Cast: Robert De Niro, Cybill Shepherd, Harvey Keitel
      Screenplay: Paul Schrader

4.   PLATOON
      1986, USA
      Director: Oliver Stone
      Cast: Tom Berenger, Willem Dafoe, Charlie Sheen
      Screenplay: Oliver Stone

5.   BARTON FINK
      1991, USA
      Director: Joel Coen
      Cast: John Turturro, John Goodman, Judy Davis
      Screenplay: Ethan Coen and Joel Coen

6.   THE NAKED GUN:
      FROM THE FILES OF POLICE SQUAD
      1988, USA
      Director: David Zucker
      Cast: Leslie Nielsen, George Kennedy, Priscilla Presley
      Screenplay: Jim Abrahams, David Zucker and Pat Proft

1. -Oh! They've encased him in Carbonite! He should be quite
   well protected. If he survived the freezing process, that is.

   Empire Strikes Back

2. -Hi, Diana Christensen. A racist lackey of the imperialist ruling
   circles. Laureen Hobbs. Badass commie nigger.

3. -They're not that different from you, are they? Same haircuts.
   Full of hormones, just like you. Invincible, just like you feel. The
   world is their oyster. They believe they're destined for great things,
   just like many of you, their eyes are full of hope, just like you.
   Did they wait until it was too late to make from their lives even
   one iota of what they were capable? Because, you see, gentle
   men, these boys are now fertilizing daffodils. But if you listen
   real close, you can hear them whisper their legacy to you.

   Dead Poets Society

4. -Love is 2 minutes 55 seconds of squelching noises.

5. -You are certainly the most distinguished group of highway
   scofflaws and degenerates ever gathered together in one place

6. -You know, the one thing I can't figure out. Are these girls
   real smart or real real lucky?
   -Don't matter. Brains'll only get you so far and luck always
   runs out.

ANSWERS >

1. **THE EMPIRE STRIKES BACK**
   1980, USA
   Director: Irwin Kershner
   Cast: Mark Hamill, Harrison Ford, Carrie Fisher
   Screenplay: George Lucas, Leigh Brackett and Lawrence Kasdan

2. **NETWORK**
   1976, USA
   Director: Sidney Lumet
   Cast: William Holden, Faye Dunaway, Peter Finch
   Screenplay: Paddy Chayefsky

3. **DEAD POETS SOCIETY**
   1989, USA
   Director: Peter Weir
   Cast: Robin Williams, Robert Sean Leonard, Ethan Hawke
   Screenplay: Tom Schulman

4. **SID & NANCY**
   1986, USA
   Director: Alex Cox
   Cast: Gary Oldman, Chloe Webb, Drew Schofield
   Screenplay: Alex Cox and Abbe Wool

5. **THE CANNONBALL RUN**
   1981, USA
   Director: Hal Needham
   Cast: Burt Reynolds, Roger Moore, Farrah Fawcett
   Screenplay: Brock Yates

6. **THELMA & LOUISE**
   1991, USA
   Director: Ridley Scott
   Cast: Susan Sarandon, Geena Davis, Harvey Keitel
   Screenplay: Callie Khouri

1. -If you want me to keep my mouth shut, it's gonna cost you some dough. I figure a thousand bucks is reasonable, so I want two.

2. -The city is made of bricks. The strong make many, the starving make few, the dead make none.

3. -I am the rocker, I am the roller, I am the out-of-controller!

4. -Lobotomy? Isn't that for loonies?
   -Not at all. Friend of mine had one. Designer of the neutron bomb. You ever hear of the neutron bomb? Destroys people - leaves buildings standing. Fits in a suitcase. It's so small, no one knows it's there until - BLAMMO! Eyes melt, skin explodes, everybody dead! So immoral, working on the thing can drive you mad. That's what happened to this friend of mine. So he had a lobotomy. Now he's well again.

5. -I don't think I've ever drunk champagne before breakfast before. With breakfast on several occasions, but never before, before.

6. -God is on our side because he hates the Yanks!
   -God is not on our side because he hates idiots also.

ANSWERS >

1. **MILLER'S CROSSING**
   1990, USA
   Director: Joel Coen
   Cast: Gabriel Byrne, Albert Finney, Marcia Gay Harden
   Screenplay: Joel Coen and Ethan Coen
   Based on the book by Dashiell Hammett

2. **THE TEN COMMANDMENTS**
   1956, USA
   Director: Cecil B Demille
   Cast: Charlton Heston, Yul Brynner, Anne Baxter
   Screenplay: J.H. Ingraham, A.E. Southon, Dorothy Clarke Wilson,
   Æneas MacKenzie, Jesse Lasky Jr., Jack Gariss and
   Fredric M. Frank.

3. **MAD MAX**
   1979, AUSTRALIA
   Director: George Miller
   Cast: Mel Gibson, Joanne Samuel, Hugh Keays Byrne
   Screenplay: James McCausland and George Miller

4. **REPO MAN**
   1984, USA
   Director: Alex Cox
   Cast: Emilio Estevez, Harry Dean Stanton, Vonetta McGee
   Screenplay: Alex Cox

5. **BREAKFAST AT TIFFANY'S**
   1961, USA
   Director: Blake Edwards
   Cast: Audrey Hepburn, George Peppard
   Screenplay: Truman Capote, George Axelrod

6. **THE GOOD, THE BAD, AND THE UGLY**
   1966, ITALY/SPAIN
   Director: Sergio Leone
   Cast: Clint Eastwood, Lee Van Cleef, Eli Wallach
   Screenplay: Luciano Vincenzoni, Sergio Leone, Agenore Incrocci and
   Furio Scarpelli

1. -It was one of those days when it's a minute away from snowing and there's this electricity in the air. You can almost hear it. And this bag was, like, dancing with me. Like a little kid begging me to play with it. For fifteen minutes. And that's the day I knew there was this entire life behind things,and... this incredibly benevolent force, that wanted me to know there was no reason to be afraid. Ever. Video's a poor excuse. But it helps me remember...and I need to remember. Sometimes, there's so much beauty in the world I feel like I can't take it, like my heart's going to cave in.

2. -You have broken what could not be broken! Hope... is... broken.

3. -I want to know more about you.
    -You already know enough about me. Any more and you're going to get a headache.

4. -When they send for you, you go in alive, you come out dead, and it's your best friend that does it.

5. I think I must have one of those faces you can't help believing.

6. -It's not you marrying me. It's me marrying anyone. I'm mentally. I can't get married to anyone - ever.

ANSWERS >

1.   AMERICAN BEAUTY
1999, USA
Director: Sam Mendes
Cast: Kevin Spacey, Annette Bening, Thora Birch
Screenplay: Alan Ball

2.   EXCALIBUR
1981, UNITED KINGDOM
Director: John Boorman
Cast: Nicol Williamson, Nigel Terry, Helen Mirren
Screenplay: Rospo Pallenberg and John Boorman
Based on the book by Thomas Malory

3.   XANADU
1980, USA
Director: Robert Greenwald
Cast: Olivia Newton John, Gene Kelly, Michael Beck
Screenplay: Richard Christian Danus and Marc Reid Rubel

4.   DONNIE BRASCO
1997, USA
Director: Mike Newell
Cast: Al Pacino, Johnny Depp, Michael Madsen
Screenplay: Paul Attanasio
Based on the book by Joseph D. Pistone and Richard Woodley

5.   PSYCHO
1960, USA
Director: Alfred Hitchcook
Cast: Anthony Perkins, Janet Leigh, Vera Miles
Screenplay: Joseph Stefano.
Based on the book by Robert Bland

6.   THE THREE FACES OF EVE
1957, USA
Director: Nunnally Johnson
Cast: Joanne Woodward, David Wayne, Lee J Cobb
Screenplay: Nunnally Johnson
Based on the book by Corbett Thigpen and Hervey M. Cleckley

1. -If I asked you to kill me, would you?
    -I don't know. How would I do it? I couldn't live without ya

2. -Hold me.
    -I can't.

3. -I dunno what the hell's in there, but it's weird and pissed
    off, whatever it is.

4. -Dave, this conversation can serve no purpose anymore.
    Goodbye.

5. -Jane, since I've met you, I've noticed things that I never knew
    were there before; birds singing, dew glistening on a newly
    formed leaf, stoplights.

6. -There's no reason to become alarmed, and we hope you'll enjoy
    the rest of your flight. By the way, is there anyone on board who
    knows how to fly a plane?
    Airplane

ANSWERS >

1.   **SID & NANCY**
     1986, USA
     Director: Alex Cox
     Cast: Gary Oldman, Chloe Webb, Drew Schofield
     Screenplay: Alex Cox and Abbe Wool

2.   **EDWARD SCISSORHANDS**
     1990, USA
     Director: Tim Burton
     Cast: Johnny Depp, Winona Ryder, Dianne West
     Screenplay: Tim Burton and Caroline Thompson

3.   **THE THING**
     1982, USA
     Director: John Carpenter
     Cast: Kurt Russell, Richard Dysart, A Wilford Brimley
     Screenplay: John W. Campbell Jr and Bill Lancaster

4.   **2001: A SPACE ODYSSEY**
     1968, UNITED KINGDOM
     Director: Stanley Kubrick
     Cast: Keir Dullea, William Sylvester, Gary Lockwood
     Screenplay: Stanley Kubrick and Arthur C. Clarke

5.   **THE NAKED GUN:**
     FROM THE FILES OF POLICE SQUAD
     1988, USA
     Director: David Zucker
     Cast: Leslie Nielsen, George Kennedy, Priscilla Presley
     Screenplay: Jim Abrahams, David Zucker and Pat Proft

6.   **AIRPLANE! / FLYING HIGH**
     1980, USA
     Director: Jim Abrahams, David Zucker, Jerry Zucker
     Cast: Robert Hays, Julie Hagerty, Robert Stack
     Screenplay: Jim Abrahams, David Zucker and Jerry Zucker

1.   -In Sicily, women are more dangerous than shotguns.

2.   -You don't fuck around with the infinite.

3.   -Do you think God knew what He was doing when He created
      woman? Huh? No shit. I really wanna know. Or do you think it
      was another one of His minor mistakes like tidal waves, earth
      quakes, FLOODS? You think women are like that? What's the
      matter? You don't think God makes mistakes? Of course He
      does. We ALL make mistakes. Of course, when WE make
      mistakes they call it evil. When GOD makes mistakes,
      they call it... nature. So whaddya think?
      Women... a mistake...or DID HE DO IT TO US ON PURPOSE?

4.   -Sometimes, you have to lose yourself 'fore you can
      find anything.

5.   I like big, fat men like you. When they fall they make more noise!

6.   -I hear you have a taste for little boys.
      -No, Caesar. Big boys.

1. THE GODFATHER
1972, USA
Director: Francis Ford Coppola
Cast: Marlon Brando, Al Pacino, James Caan
Screenplay: Mario Puzo and Francis Ford Coppola
Based on the book by Mario Puzo

2. MEAN STREETS
1973, USA
Director: Martin Scorsese
Cast: Robert De Niro, Harvey Keitel, David Proval
Screenplay: Martin Scorsese and Mardik Martin

3. THE WITCHES OF EASTWICK
1987, USA
Director: George Miller
Cast: Jack Nicholson, Cher, Susan Sarandon
Screenplay: Michael Cristofe.
Based on the book by John Updike

4. DELIVERANCE
1972, USA
Director: John Boorman
Cast: Jon Voight, Burt Reynolds, Ned Beatty
Screenplay: James Dickey
Based on the book by James Dickey

5. THE GOOD, THE BAD, AND THE UGLY
1966, ITALY/SPAIN
Director: Sergio Leone
Cast: Clint Eastwood, Lee Van Cleef, Eli Wallach
Screenplay: Luciano Vincenzoni, Sergio Leone, Agenore Incrocci and Furio Scarpelli

6. CALIGULA
1980, ITALY/USA
Director: Tinto Brass
Cast: Malcolm McDowell, Peter O'Toole, Teresa Ann Savoy
Screenplay: Gore Vidal, Bob Guccione, Giancarlo Lui, Masolino D'Amico, Franco Rossellini and Roberto Rossellini

1. -Don't be alarmed, Ladies and Gentlemen. Those chains are made of chrome steel.

2. -And you know what they call a... a... a Quarter Pounder with Cheese in Paris?
    -They don't call it a Quarter Pounder with cheese?
    -No man, they got the metric system. They wouldn't know what the fuck a Quarter Pounder is.
    -Then what do they call it?
    -They call it a Royale with cheese.
    -A Royale with cheese! What do they call a Big Mac?
    -A Big Mac's a Big Mac, but they call it le Big-Mac.
    -Le Big-Mac! Ha ha ha ha! What do they call a Whopper?
    -I dunno, I didn't go to no Burger King.

    Pulp Fiction

3. -Dave...my mind is going...I can feel it...I can feel it.

    2001

4. -You have brought music back in to my life. I had forgotten.

5. -I'd like to see you with your pants off, Mr. Reed.

6. -Hi, man.
    -What are you doing?!
    -I'm drinking wine and eating cheese, and catching some rays, you know ...

1.   KING KONG
        1976, USA
        Director: John Guillermin
        Cast: Jeff Bridges, Charles Grodin, Jessica Lange
        Screenplay: Merian C. Cooper, Edgar Wallace, James Ashmore
        Creelman, Ruth Rose and Lorenzo Semple Jr.

2.   PULP FICTION
        1994, USA
        Director: Quentin Tarantino
        Cast: John Travolta, Samuel L Jackson, Uma Thurman
        Screenplay: Quentin Tarantino and Roger Avary

3.   2001: A SPACE ODYSSEY
        1968, UNITED KINGDOM
        Director: Stanley Kubrick
        Cast: Keir Dullea, William Sylvester, Gary Lockwood
        Screenplay: Stanley Kubrick and Arthur C. Clarke

4.   THE SOUND OF MUSIC
        1965, USA
        Director: Robert Wise
        Cast: Julie Andrews, Christopher Plummer, Eleanor Parker
        Screenplay: Ernest Lehman, Richard Rodgers and
        Oscar Hammerstein II, Howard Lindsay and Russel Crouse

5.   REDS
        1981, USA
        Director: Warren Beatty
        Cast: Warren Beatty, Diane Keaton, Edward Herrmann
        Screenplay: Warren Beatty, Trevor Griffiths, Elaine May, John Reed (II),
        Jeremy Pikser and Peter S. Feibleman

6.   KELLY'S HEROES
        1970, USA
        Director: Brian G Hutton
        Cast: Clint Eastwood, Telly Savalas, Don Rickles
        Screenplay: Troy Kennedy-Martin

1.   -This kind of certainty comes but once in a lifetime.

2.   -I only get carsick on boats.

3.   -The best people all shave twice a day.

4.   -Man, I see in Fight Club the strongest and smartest men who've
     ever lived. I see all this potential, and I see squandering. God
     damn it, an entire generation pumping gas, waiting tables; slaves
     with white collars. Advertising has us chasing cars and clothes,
     working jobs we hate so we can buy shit we don't need. We're
     the middle children of history, man. No purpose or place. We have
     no Great War. No Great Depression. Our Great War's a spiritual
     war... our Great Depression is our lives. We've all been raised on
     television to believe that one day we'd all be millionaires, and
     movie gods, and rock stars. But we won't. And we're slowly
     learning that fact. And we're very, very pissed off.

     Fight Club

5.   -I pray that I may never see the desert again. Hear me, God.

6.   -My idea of Heaven is a solid white nightclub with me as a
     headliner for all eternity, and they LOVE me.

1. **THE BRIDGES OF MADISON COUNTY**
   1995, USA
   Director: Clint Eastwood
   Cast: Clint Eastwood, Meryl Streep, Annie Corley
   Screenplay: Richard LaGravenese
   Based on the book by Robert James Waller

2. **MIDNIGHT COWBOY**
   1969, USA
   Director: John Schlesinger
   Cast: Dustin Hoffman, Jon Voight, Sylvia Miles
   Screenplay: Waldo Salt
   Based on the book by James Leo Herlihy

3. **LOLITA**
   1962, UNITED KINGDOM
   Director: Stanley Kubrick
   Cast: James Mason, Shelley Winters, Peter Sellers
   Screenplay: Vladimir Nabokov and Stanley Kubrick
   Based on the book by Vladimir Nabokov

4. **FIGHT CLUB**
   1999, USA
   Director: David Fincher
   Cast: Brad Pitt, Edward Norton, Helena Bonham Carter
   Screenplay: Jim Uhls
   Based on the book by Chuck Palahniuk

5. **LAWRENCE OF ARABIA**
   1962, UNITED KINGDOM
   Director: David Lean
   Cast: Peter O'Toole, Alec Guinness, Anthony Quinn
   Screenplay: T.E. Lawrence, Robert Bolt and Michael Wilson

6. **THE EXORCIST**
   1973, USA
   Director: William Friedkin
   Cast: Ellen Burstyn, Max Von Sydow, Linda Blair
   Screenplay: William Peter Blatty

1. -I've never seen you take a drink in your life.
   -Honey, there are a lot of things you ain't never seen me do.
   That's no sign I don't do 'em.

2. -The wind opens the sea.
   -God opens the sea with a blast of his nostrils.

3. -What would you call that hairstyle you're wearing?
   -Arthur.

4. -At least we've got it stopped.
   -Yeah, as long as the Arctic stays cold.

5. -I don't want to put a wad of white powder in my nose.
   There's the nasal membrane...
   -You never want to try anything new, Alvy.
   -How can you say that? Whose idea was it? I said that you,
   I and that girl from your acting class should sleep together
   in a threesome.
   -Well, that's sick!
   -Yeah, I know it's sick, but it's new. You didn't say it couldn't
   be sick.

6. -Boys, you got to learn not to talk to nuns that way.

ANSWERS >

1. **THE THREE FACES OF EVE**
    1957, USA
    Director: Nunnally Johnson
    Cast: Joanne Woodward, David Wayne, Lee J Cobb
    Screenplay: Nunnally Johnson
    Based on the book by Corbett Thigpen and Hervey M. Cleckley

2. **THE TEN COMMANDMENTS**
    1956, USA
    Director: Cecil B Demille
    Cast: Charlton Heston, Yul Brynner, Anne Baxter
    Screenplay: J.H. Ingraham, A.E. Southon, Dorothy Clarke Wilson,
    Æneas MacKenzie, Jesse Lasky Jr., Jack Gariss and
    Fredric M. Frank

3. **A HARD DAY'S NIGHT**
    1964, UNITED KINGDOM
    Director: Richard Lester
    Cast: John Lennon, Paul McCartney, George Harrison
    Screenplay: Alun Owen

4. **THE BLOB**
    1958, USA
    Director:Irwin S. Yeaworth Jr.
    Cast: Steve McQueen, Aneta Corsaut, Earl Rowe
    Screenplay: Kay Linaker, Irwing H. Millgate

5. **ANNIE HALL**
    1977, USA
    Director: Woody Allen
    Cast: Woody Allen, Diane Keaton, Tony Roberts
    Screenplay: Woody Allen and Marshall Brickman

6. **THE BLUES BROTHERS**
    1980, USA
    Director: John Landis
    Cast: John Belushi, Dan Aykroyd, Cap Calloway
    Screenplay: Dan Aykroyd and John Landis

1. -Rhett... If you go ... where shall I go? What shall I do?
   -Frankly, my dear, I don't give a damn.

   Gone With the Wind

2. -This time, John Wayne does not walk off into the sunset
   with Grace Kelly.
   -That was Gary Cooper, Asshole.

3. -Your tongue is old but sharp, Cicero. Be careful how you wag
   it. One day it will cut off your head.

4. -So, your fawtha was a Woman. Who was he?
   -He was a Centurion, in the Jeruselem Garrison.
   -What was his name?
   -Nottius Maximus, sir.
   -Centuwion do you have anyone in your gawwison by that name?
   -No, sir.
   -Well you seem awfully sure. Have you checked?
   -I think its a joke, sir. Sort of like...uh...Sillius Sodus,
   or Biggus Dickus.

   Life of Brian

5. -The reality is that we do not wash our own laundry.
   It just gets dirtier.

6. -The richest man is the one with the most powerful friends.

ANSWERS >

1.   GONE WITH THE WIND
        1939, USA
        Director: Victor Fleming
        Cast: Clark Gable, Vivien Leigh, Leslie Howard
        Screenplay: Sidney Howard, Ben Hecht, David O. Selznick, Jo
        Swerling and John Van Druten. Based on the book by Margaret
        Mitchell

2.   DIE HARD
        1988, USA
        Director: John McTiernan
        Cast: Bruce Willis, Alan Rickman, Bonnie Bedelia
        Screenplay: Jeb Stuart and Steven E. de Souza
        Based on the book by Roderick Thorp

3.   CLEOPATRA
        1963, USA
        Director: Joseph L Mankiewicz
        Cast: Elizabeth Taylor, Richard Burton, Rex Harrison
        Screenplay: Sidney Buchman, Ben Hecht, Ranald MacDougall and
        Joseph L. Mankiewicz
        Based on the book by Carlo Mario Franzero

4.   MONTY PYTHON'S LIFE OF BRIAN
        1979, UNITED KINGDOM
        Director: Terry Jones
        Cast: Graham Chapman, John Cleese, Terry Gilliam
        Screenplay: Graham Chapman, John Cleese, Terry Gilliam, Eric Idle,
        Terry Jones and Michael Palin

5.   SERPICO
        1973, USA
        Director: Sidney Lumet
        Cast: Al Pacino, John Randolph, Jack Kehoe
        Screenplay: Waldo Salt and Norman Wexler
        Based on the book by Peter Maas

6.   THE GODFATHER PART III
        1990, USA
        Director: Francis Ford Coppola
        Cast: Al Pacino, Diane Keaton, Talia Shire
        Screenplay: Mario Puzo and Francis Ford Coppola

1. -I'd like an omelet, plain, and a chicken salad sandwich on wheat toast, no mayonnaise, no butter, no lettuce. And a cup of coffee.
    -A #2, chicken salad sand. Hold the butter, the lettuce, the mayonnaise, and a cup of coffee. Anything else?
    -Yeah, now all you have to do is hold the chicken, bring me the toast, give me a check for the chicken salad sandwich, and you haven't broken any rules.
    -You want me to hold the chicken, huh?
    -I want you to hold it between your knees.

2. -Get up, boy. I bet you can squeal. I bet you can squeal like a pig.

3. -The human spirit is more powerful than any drug - and that's what needs to be nourished.

4. -Just how bad is it?
    -It's a fire. All fires are bad.

5. -After all ... tomorrow is another day.

    Gone with the Wind

6. -Monsieur Rick, what kind of a man is Captain Renault?
    -Oh, he's just like any other man, only more so.

ANSWERS >

1. **FIVE EASY PIECES**
   1970, USA
   Director: Bob Rafelson
   Cast: Jack Nicholson, Karen Black, Billy Green
   Screenplay: Carole Eastman and Bob Rafelson

2. **DELIVERANCE**
   1972, USA
   Director: John Boorman
   Cast: Jon Voight, Burt Reynolds, Ned Beatty
   Screenplay: James Dickey
   Based on the book by James Dickey

3. **AWAKENINGS**
   1990, USA
   Director: Penny Marshall
   Cast: Robert De Niro, Robin Williams, Julie Kavner
   Screenplay: Steven Zaillian
   Based on the book by Oliver Sacks

4. **THE TOWERING INFERNO**
   1974, USA
   Director: John Guillermin, Irwin Allen
   Cast: Steve Mcqueen, Paul Newman, William Holden
   Screenplay: Stirling Silliphant
   Based on the book by Richard Martin Stern, Thomas N. Scortia and
   Frank M. Robinson

5. **GONE WITH THE WIND**
   1939, USA
   Director: Victor Fleming
   Cast: Clark Gable, Vivien Leigh, Leslie Howard
   Screenplay: Sidney Howard, Ben Hecht, David O. Selznick, Jo
   Swerling and John Van Druten
   Based on the book by Margaret Mitchell

6. **CASABLANCA**
   1942, USA
   Director: Michael Curtiz
   Cast: Humphrey Bogart, Ingrid Bergman, Paul Henreid
   Screenplay: Murray Burnett, Joan Alison, Julius J. Epstein, Philip G.
   Epstein, Howard K and, Casey Robinson

1. -I've been in prison for three years. My dick gets hard if the wind blows.

2. -I'm tapped out, Marv. American Express' got a hit man lookin' for me.

3. -Have you no human consideration?
   -Show me a human, and I might have!

4. -Where am I?
   -You're in the records room.
   -Oh. Do you have the Beatles White Album? Never mind, just bring me a cup of hot fat. And the head of Alfredo Garcia.

5. -Still wearing your gun on your ankle? Somebody told me the reason you did that was so when you met a chick and rubbed against her she wouldn't know you were a cop. I said that was bullshit. It must be some kind of fast-draw gimmick or something.

6. -You kill anybody?
   -A few cops
   -No real people?
   -Just cops.

ANSWERS >

1. **48HRS**
   1982, USA
   Director: Walter Hill
   Cast: Nick Nolte, Eddie Murphy, Annette O'Toole
   Screenplay: Roger Spottiswoode, Walter Hill, Larry Gross,
   Steven E. de Souza and Jeb Stuart

2. **WALL STREET**
   1987, USA
   Director: Oliver Stone
   Cast: Michael Douglas, Charlie Sheen, Daryl Hannah
   Screenplay: Stanley Weiser and Oliver Stone

3. **ALL ABOUT EVE**
   1950, USA
   Director: Joseph L Mankiewicz
   Cast: Bette Davis, Anne Baxter, George Sanders
   Screenplay: Joseph L. Mankiewicz and Mary Orr

4. **FLETCH**
   1985, USA
   Director: Michael Ritchie
   Cast: Chevy Chase, Dana Wheeler Nicholson, Tim Matheson
   Screenplay: Andrew Bergman
   Based on the book by Gregory McDonald

5. **THE FRENCH CONNECTION**
   1971, USA
   Director: William Friedkin
   Cast: Gene Hackman, Fernando Rey, Roy Scheider
   Screenplay: Ernest Tidyman, Edward M. Keyes
   Based on the book avRobin Moore

6. **RESERVOIR DOGS**
   1992, USA
   Director: Quentin Tarantino
   Cast: Harvey Keitel, Tim Roth, Michael Madsen
   Screenplay: Roger Avary and Quentin Tarantino

1. -...and as they both sink beneath the waves, the frog cries out, Why did you sting me, Mr. Scorpion? For now we both will drown! Scorpion replies, I can't help it. It's in my nature!.

2. -Winning that ticket, Rose, was the best thing that ever happened to me. It brought me to you. And I'm thankful for that, Rose. I'm thankful. You must do me this honor, Rose. Promise me you'll survive. That you won't give up, no matter what happens, no matter how hopeless. Promise me now, Rose, and never let go of that promise.

    Titanic

3. -You ever wished you were someone else?
    -I'd like to try being Porky Pig.
    -I never wanted to be anyone else.

4. -If you want a simple yes or no, you're gonna have to finish the question.

5. -When you're a Jet your a Jet all the way; from you're first cigarette until your last dying day!

6. -What will we do when we have lost the war?
    -Prepare for the next one.

1. THE CRYING GAME
   1992, UNITED KINGDOM
   Director: Neil Jordan
   Cast: Stephan Rea, Miranda Richardson, Forest Whitaker
   Screenplay: Neil Jordan

2. TITANIC
   1997, USA
   Director: James Cameron
   Cast: Leonardo Dicaprio, Kate Winslet, Billy Zane
   Screenplay: James Cameron

3. EASY RIDER
   1969, USA
   Director: Dennis Hopper
   Cast: Peter Fonda, Dennis Hopper, Jack Nicholson
   Screenplay: Peter Fonda, Dennis Hopper and Terry Southern

4. BUGSY
   1991, USA
   Director: Barry Levinson
   Cast: Warren Beatty, Annette Bening, Harvey Keitel
   Screenplay: James Toback
   Based on the book by Dean Jennings

5. WEST SIDE STORY
   1961, USA
   Director: Robert Wise, Jerome Robbins
   Cast: Natalie Wood, Richard Beymer, George Chakiris
   Screenplay: Jerome Robbins, Arthur Laurents and Ernest Lehman
   Based on the play "Romeo and Juliet" by William Shakespeare

6. CROSS OF IRON
   1977, UNITED KINGDOM/WESTGERMANY
   Director: Sam Peckinpah
   Cast: James Coburn, Maximilian Schell, James Mason
   Screenplay: Julius J. Epstein, James Hamilton and Walter Kelley
   Based on the book by Frederick Forsyth

1. -Is it safe? Is it safe?
    -You're talking to me?
    -Is it safe?
    -What safe?
    -Is it safe?
    -I don't know what you mean. I can't tell you something's safe
    or not, unless I know specifically what you're talking about.
    -Is it safe?
    -Tell me what it is first.
    -Is it safe?
    -Yes, it's safe. It's very safe. So safe you wouldn't believe it.
    -Is it safe?
    -No, it's not safe. It's very dangerous. Be careful.

2. -He won't get far on hot air and fantasy.

3. -Let's have an intelligent conversation here: I'll talk,
    and you listen.

4. -Stanley, see this? This is this. This ain't something else.
    This is this!

5. -A prayer's as good as a bayonet on a day like this.

ANSWERS >

1. **MARATHON MAN**
   1976, USA
   Director: John Schlesinger
   Cast: Dustin Hoffman, Laurence Olivier, Roy Scheider
   Screenplay: Robert Towne and William Goldman
   Based on the book by William Goldman

2. **THE ADVENTURES OF BARON MUNCHAUSEN**
   1989, UNITED KINGDOM
   Director: Terry Gilliam
   Cast: John Neville, Eric Idle, Sarah Polley
   Screenplay: Terry Gilliam and Charles McKeown
   Based on the book by Rudolph Erich Raspe

3. **WATERWORLD**
   1995, USA
   Director: Kevin Reynolds
   Cast: Kevin Costner, Dennis Hopper, Jeanne Tripplehorn
   Screenplay: Peter Rader and David Twohy

4. **THE DEER HUNTER**
   1978, USA
   Director: Michael Cimino
   Cast: Robert De Niro, Christopher Walken, Meryl Streep
   Screenplay: Michael Cimino, Louis Garfinkle, Quinn K. Redeker and
   Deric Washburn

5. **ZULU**
   1963, UNITED KINGDOM
   Director: Cy Endfield
   Cast: Stanley Baker, Jack Hawkins, Ulla Jacobsson
   Screenplay: John Prebble, John Prebble and Cy Endfield

1.   -You can't fight in here. This is the War Room!

2.   -It means she can't be a witness for us. In fact, when the
      defense finds her - and they will - she'll be a witness for them!

3.   -Play it once, Sam. For old time's sake.
      -I don't know what you mean, Miss Elsa.
      -Play it, Sam. Play As time goes by.

      Casablanca

4.   -You said bullshit and experience is all it takes, right?
      -Right.
      -Come on in and experience some of my bullshit.

5.   -A guy once told me, Do not have any attachments, do not
      have anything in your life you are not willing to walk out on in
      30 seconds flat if you spot the heat around the corner.

6.   -Henry, I have some reports here from your Major O'Houlihan
      that I, frankly, find hard to believe.
      -Well, don't believe them then, General. Good-bye.

ANSWERS >

1. **DR STRANGELOVE OR: HOW I LEARNED TO STOP WORRYING AND LOVE THE BOMB**
   1963, UNITED KINGDOM
   Director: Stanley Kubrick
   Cast: Peter Sellers, George C Scott, Sterling Hayden
   Screenplay: Stanley Kubrick, Terry Southern and Peter George III
   Based on the book by Peter George

2. **THE ACCUSED**
   1988, USA
   Director: Jonathan Kaplan
   Cast: Kelly McGillis, Jodie Foster, Bernie Coulson
   Screenplay: Tom Topor

3. **CASABLANCA**
   1942, USA
   Director: Michael Curtiz
   Cast: Humphrey Bogart, Ingrid Bergman, Paul Henreid
   Screenplay: Murray Burnett, Joan Alison, Julius J. Epstein,
   Philip G. Epstein, Howard K and, Casey Robinson

4. **48 HRS**
   1982, USA
   Director: Walter Hill
   Cast: Nick Nolte, Eddie Murphy, Annette O'Toole
   Screenplay: Roger Spottiswoode, Walter Hill, Larry Gross,
   Steven E. de Souza and Jeb Stuart

5. **HEAT**
   1995, USA
   Director: Michael Mann
   Cast: Al Pacino, Robert De Niro, Val Kilmer
   Screenplay: Michael Mann

6. **MASH**
   1970, USA
   Director: Robert Altman
   Cast: Donald Sutherland, Elliott Gould, Tom Skerritt
   Screenplay: Ring Lardner Jr.
   Based on the book by Richard Hooker

1. -Why am / Mr. Pink?
    -Cause you're a faggot, that's why!

    Reservoir Dogs

2. -You know...there is really nothing the living can do to bring back
    the dead.

3. -I don't feel I have to wipe everybody out, Tom.
    Just my enemies.

4. -We can't bury Cheryl. She's our friend.

5. -E.T. phone home.

    E.T.

6. -What kind of childhood did you have?
    -Short.

ANSWERS >

1. **RESERVOIR DOGS**
   1992, USA
   Director: Quentin Tarantino
   Cast: Harvey Keitel, Tim Roth, Michael Madsen
   Screenplay: Roger Avary and Quentin Tarantino

2. **THE TOWERING INFERNO**
   1974, USA
   Director: John Guillermin, Irwin Allen
   Cast: Steve Mcqueen, Paul Newman, William Holden
   Screenplay: Stirling Silliphant
   Based on the book by Richard Martin Stern, Thomas N. Scortia and
   Frank M. Robinson

3. **THE GODFATHER PART II**
   1974, USA
   Director: Francis Ford Coppola
   Cast: Al Pacino, Robert De Niro, Robert Duvall,
   Screenplay: Mario Puzo and Francis Ford Coppola

4. **THE EVIL DEAD**
   1983, USA
   Director: Sam Raimi
   Cast: Bruce Campbell, Ellen Sandweiss, Hal Delrich
   Screenplay: Sam Raimi

5. **E.T THE EXTRATERRESTRIAL**
   1982, USA
   Director: Steven Spielberg
   Cast: Dee Wallace, Henry Thomas, Peter Coyote
   Screenplay: Melissa Mathison

6. **ESCAPE FROM ALCATRAZ**
   1979, USA
   Director: Donald Siegel
   Cast: Clint Eastwood, Patrick McGoohan, Roberts Blossom
   Screenplay: Richard Tuggle
   Based on the book by J. Campbell Bruce

1. -Where the Lord closes a door,
    somewhere He opens a window.

    Sound of Music

2. -Well, we went skinny dipping, and we did things that frightened
    the fish.

3. -You're like the thief who isn't the least bit sorry he stole,
    but is terribly, terribly sorry he's going to jail.

    Gone w/ the Wind

4. -Disturbing the peace? I got thrown out of a window! What's
    the fucking charge for getting pushed out of a moving car, huh?
    Jaywalking?!

5. -Martha, in my mind, you're buried in cement right up to the
    neck. No, up to the nose, it's much quieter.

6. -That's the damndest thing I ever saw! I don't know... it seemed
    to swoop down at you deliberately!

ANSWERS >

1.   THE SOUND OF MUSIC
   1965, USA
   Director: Robert Wise
   Cast: Julie Andrews, Christopher Plummer, Eleanor Parker
   Screenplay: Ernest Lehman, Richard Rodgers and Oscar
   Hammerstein II, Howard Lindsay and Russel Crouse

2.   STEEL MAGNOLIAS
   1989, USA
   Director: Herbert Ross
   Cast: Sally Field, Dolly Parton, Julia Roberts
   Screenplay: Robert Harling

3.   GONE WITH THE WIND
   1939, USA
   Director: Victor Fleming
   Cast: Clark Gable, Vivien Leigh, Leslie Howard
   Screenplay: Sidney Howard, Ben Hecht, David O. Selznick, Jo
   Swerling and John Van Druten
   Based on the book by Margaret Mitchell

4.   BEVERLY HILLS COP
   1984, USA
   Director: Martin Brest
   Cast: Eddie Murphy, Judge Reinhold, John Ashton
   Screenplay: Danilo Bach and Daniel Petrie Jr.

5.   WHO'S AFRAID OF VIRGINIA WOOLF?
   1966, USA
   Director: Mike Nichols
   Cast: Elizabeth Taylor, Richard Burton, George Segal
   Screenplay: Edward Albee and Ernest Lehman

6.   THE BIRDS
   1963, USA
   Director: Alfred Hitchcock
   Cast: Rod Taylor, Tippi Hedren, Jessica Tandy
   Screenplay: Daphne Du Maurier and Evan Hunter

1. -You don't know how hard it is being a woman looking the way I do.
   -You don't know how hard it is being a man looking at the woman looking the way you do.

2. -There are never enough hours in the days of a queen, and her nights have too many.

   Cleopatra

3. -Generally, you don't see that kind of behavior in a major appliance.

4. -If he'd just pay me what he's paying them to stop me robbing him, I'd stop robbing him!

5. -A repo man spends his life getting into tense situations.

6. -Hey, Leatherface! Come help me with Grandpa!

ANSWERS >

1. WHO FRAMED ROGER RABBIT
    1988, USA
    Director: Robert Zemeckis
    Cast: Bob Hoskins, Christopher Lloyd, Joanna Cassidy
    Screenplay: Jeffrey Price and Peter S. Seaman
    Based on the book by Gary K. Wolf

2. CLEOPATRA
    1963, USA
    Director: Joseph L Mankiewicz
    Cast: Elizabeth Taylor, Richard Burton, Rex Harrison
    Screenplay: Sidney Buchman, Ben Hecht, Ranald MacDougall and
    Joseph L. Mankiewicz. Based on the book by Carlo Mario Franzero

3. GHOSTBUSTERS
    1984, USA
    Director: Ivan Reitman
    Cast: Bill Murray, Dan Aykroyd, Harold Ramis
    Screenplay: Dan Aykroyd, Harold Ramis and Rick Moranis

4. BUTCH CASSIDY AND THE SUNDANCE KID
    1969, USA
    Director: George Roy Hill
    Cast: Paul Newman, Robert Redford, Katharine Ross
    Screenplay: William Goldman

5. REPO MAN
    1984, USA
    Director: Alex Cox
    Cast: Emilio Estevez, Harry Dean Stanton, Vonetta McGee
    Screenplay: Alex Cox

6. THE TEXAS CHAINSAW MASSACRE
    1974, USA
    Director: Tobe Hopper
    Cast: Marilyn Burns, Gunner Hansen, Ed Neal
    Screenplay: Kim Henkel and Tobe Hooper

1. -Sorry boys. All the stitches in the world can't sew me back together again.

2. -Henry, I have some reports here from your Major O'Houlihan that I frankly find hard to believe.
    -Well, don't believe them then, General. Good-bye.

    Mash

3. -What have you been doing all these years?
    -I've been going to bed early.

4. -It's Halloween! Everyone's entitled to one good scare.

5. -Meyer, we have known each other since we were too young to fuck.

6. -Just because some kid smashes into your wife on the turnpike doesn't make it a crime to be seventeen.

   ANSWERS >

1.   CARLITO'S WAY
     1993, USA
     Director: Brian De Palma
     Cast: Al Pacino, Sean Penn, Penelope Ann Miller
     Screenplay: David Koepp
     Based on the book by Edwin Torres

2.   MASH
     1970, USA
     Director: Robert Altman
     Cast: Donald Sutherland, Elliott Gould, Tom Skerritt
     Screenplay: Ring Lardner Jr.
     Based on the book by Richard Hooker

3.   ONCE UPON A TIME IN AMERICA
     1984, USA
     Director: Sergio Leone
     Cast: Robert De Niro, James Woods, Elizabeth McGovern
     Screenplay: Leonardo Benvenuti, Piero De Bernardi, Enrico Medioli,
     Franco Arcalli, Franco Ferrini, Sergio Leone, Stuart Kaminsky and
     Ernesto Gastaldi
     Based on the book by Harry Grey (II)

4.   HALLOWEEN
     1978, USA
     Director: John Carpenter
     Cast: Donald Pleasence, Jamie Lee Curtis, Nancy Loomis
     Screenplay: John Carpenter and Debra Hill

5.   BUGSY
     1991, USA
     Director: Barry Levinson
     Cast: Warren Beatty, Annette Bening, Harvey Keitel
     Screenplay: James Toback
     Based on the book by Dean Jennings

6.   THE BLOB
     1958, USA
     Director:Irwin S. Yeaworth Jr.
     Cast: Steve McQueen, Aneta Corsaut, Earl Rowe
     Screenplay: Kay Linaker, Irwing H. Millgate

1. -Boards don't hit back.

2. -Hippy, you think everything is a conspiracy.
    -Everything is.

3. -Frankly, you're beginning to smell, and for a stud in New York,
    that's a handicap.

4. -Do you believe in God?
    -The question is: does God believe in me?

5. -I know, I know. We are your chosen people. But, once in
    a while, can't you choose someone else?

6. -Well, I don't like to see things goin' good or bad. I like 'em
    in between.

   ANSWERS >

1.   ENTER THE DRAGON
        1973, USA
        Director: Robert Clouse
        Cast: Bruce Lee, John Saxon, Jim Kelly
        Screenplay: Michael Allin

2.   THE ABYSS
        1989, USA
        Director: James Cameron
        Cast: Ed Harris, Mary Elizabeth Mastrantonio, Michael Biehn
        Screenplay: James Cameron

3.   MIDNIGHT COWBOY
        1969, USA
        Director: John Schlesinger
        Cast: Dustin Hoffman, Jon Voight, Sylvia Miles
        Screenplay: Waldo Salt
        Based on the book by James Leo Herlihy

4.   LOLITA
        1962, UNITED KINGDOM
        Director: Stanley Kubrick
        Cast: James Mason, Shelley Winters, Peter Sellers
        Screenplay: Vladimir Nabokov and Stanley Kubrick
        Based on the book by Vladimir Nabokov

5.   FIDDLER ON THE ROOF
        1971, USA
        Director: Norman Jewison
        Cast: (Chaim) Topol, Norma Crane, Leonard Frey
        Screenplay: Joseph Stein
        Based on the book by Sholom Aleichem

6.   RED RIVER
        1948, USA
        Director: Howard Hawks
        Cast: John Wayne, Montgomery Clift, Walter Brennan
        Screenplay: Borden Chase, Borden Chase and Charles Schnee

1.   -I do wish we could chat longer, but I'm having an old friend
     for dinner. Bye.

2.   -Is this where you live?
     -Who lives?

3.   -I'm the best you ever seen, Fats. I'm the best there is.
     Even if you beat me, I'm still the best.

4.   -That's too bad. I was going to marry her. I already
     put a deposit on twin cemetery plots.

5.   It only took me one night to realize that if brains were dynamite,
     you couldn't even blow your nose.

6.   -Never! I'll never turn to the Dark Side! You've failed, your
     highness. I am a Jedi, like my father before me.

     Return of the Jedi

1. THE SILENCE OF THE LAMBS
    1991, USA
    Director: Jonathan Demme
    Cast: Jodie Foster, Anthony Hopkins, Scott Glenn
    Screenplay: Ted Tally
    Based on the book by Thomas Harris

2. REBEL WITHOUT A CAUSE
    1955, USA
    Director: Nicholas Ray
    Cast: James Dean, Natalie Wood, Sal Mineo
    Screenplay: Nicholas Ray, Irving Shulman and Stewart Stern

3. THE HUSTLER
    1961, USA
    Director: Robert Rossen
    Cast: Paul Newman, Jackie Gleason, Piper Laurie
    Screenplay: Sidney Carroll and Robert Rossen
    Based on the book by Walter Tevis

4. WHAT'S UP TIGER LILY?
    1966, JAPAN
    Director: Senkichi Taniguchi
    Cast: Tatsuya Mihashi, Miya Hana, Eiko Wakabayashi
    Screenplay: Woody Allen, Julie Bennett, Frank Buxton, Louise Lasser,
    Len Maxwell, Mickey Rose and Bryan Wilson

5. AMERICAN GRAFFITI
    1973, USA
    Director: George Lucas
    Cast: Richard Dreyfuss, Ronny Howard, Paul LeMat
    Screenplay: George Lucas, Gloria Katz and Willard Huyck

6. RETURN OF THE JEDI
    1983, USA
    Director: Richard Marquand
    Cast: Mark Hamill, Harrison Ford, Carrie Fisher
    Screenplay: George Lucas and Lawrence Kasdan

1.　　-How do you feel?
　　　-Like the kling klang king of the rim ram room.

2.　　-The only arithmetic he ever got was hearing the referee
　　　count up to ten.

3.　　-He's more machine now than man; twisted and evil.

　　　Return of the Jedi

4.　　-Excuse me, are the voices inside my head bothering you?

5.　　-Seven schools in seven states and the only thing different
　　　is my locker combination.

6.　　-You give me powders, pills, baths, injections,
　　　enemas - when all I need is love.

ANSWERS >

1.   **LEAVING LAS VEGAS**
   1995, USA
   Director: Mike Figgis
   Cast: Nicolas Cage, Elisabeth Shue, Julian Sands
   Screenplay: Mike Figgis
   Based on the book by John O'Brien

2.   **WATERFRONT**
   1950 UNITED KINGDOM
   Director: Michael Anderson
   Cast: Robert Newton, Kathleen Harrison
   Screenplay: John Brophy, Paul Soskin

3.   **RETURN OF THE JEDI**
   1983, USA
   Director: Richard Marquand
   Cast: Mark Hamill, Harrison Ford, Carrie Fisher
   Screenplay: George Lucas and Lawrence Kasdan

4.   **THE GODS MUST BE CRAZY**
   1980, BOTSWANA
   Director: Jamie Uys
   Cast: Marius Weyers, Sandra Prinsloo, N!xau
   Screenplay: Jamie Uys

5.   **HEATHERS**
   1989, USA
   Director: Michael Lehmann
   Cast: Winona Ryder, Christian Slater, Shannen Doherty
   Screenplay: Daniel Waters

6.   **THE BRIDGE ON THE RIVER KWAI**
   1957, UNITED KINGDOM
   Director: David Lean
   Cast: William Holden, Alec Guinness, Jack Hwakins
   Screenplay: Michael Wilson, Carl Foreman.
   Based on the book by Pierre Boulle

1. -I'm just a sweet transvestite... from Transsexual... Transylvania.

2. -Sometimes I don't know where the bullshit ends and the truth begins.

3. -First learn stand, then learn fly. Nature's rule, Daniel-san, not mine.

4. -Now listen to me - all of you! You are all condemned men. We keep you alive to serve this ship. So row well, and live.

5. -There's been a lamp burning in the window for ya, honey.
   -No thanks, I jumped out that window a long time ago.

6. -I'm going next. So if ole' fat ass gets stuck, I won't get stuck behind her!

ANSWERS >

1. **THE ROCKY HORROR PICTURE SHOW**
   1975, USA
   Director: Jim Sharman
   Cast: Tim Curry, Susan Sarandon, Barry Bostwick
   Screenplay: Richard O'Brien, Jim Sharman

2. **ALL THAT JAZZ**
   1979, USA
   Director: Bob Fosse
   Cast: Roy Schneider, Jessica Lange, Ann Reinking
   Screenplay: Robert Alan Aurthur and Bob Fosse

3. **THE KARATE KID**
   1984, USA
   Director: John G Avildsen
   Cast: Ralph Macchio, Noriyuki Morita, Elisabeth Shue
   Screenplay: Robert Mark Kamen

4. **BEN-HUR**
   1959, USA
   Director: William Wyler
   Cast: Charlton Heston, Jack Hawkins, Stephen Boyd
   Screenplay: Karl Tunberg, Maxwell Anderson, Christopher Fry and
   Gore Vidal
   Based on the book by Lew Wallace

5. **HIS GIRL FRIDAY**
   1940, USA
   Director: Howard Hawks
   Cast: Cary Grant, Rosalind Russell, Ralph Bellamy
   Screenplay: Ben Hecht, Charles MacArthur and Charles Lederer

6. **THE POSEIDON ADVENTURE**
   1972, USA
   Director: Ronald Neame
   Cast: Gene Hackman, Ernest Borgnine, Red Buttons
   Screenplay: Wendell Mayes and Stirling Silliphant
   Based on the book by Paul Gallico

1.   -Just when I thought that I was out they pull me back in.

2.   -Which one of you nuts has got any guts?

3.   -No matter what anybody tells you, words and ideas can
      change the world.

4.   -All those moments will be lost in time, like tears in rain.

5.   -Don't kid yourself, Francesca. You are anything but
      a simple woman.

6.   -I'm young, I'm handsome, I'm fast, I'm pretty and I can't
      possibly be beat.

1. **THE GODFATHER PART III**
   1990, USA
   Director: Francis Ford Coppola
   Cast: Al Pacino, Diane Keaton, Talia Shire
   Screenplay: Mario Puzo and Francis Ford Coppola

2. **ONE FLEW OVER THE CUCKOO'S NEST**
   1975, USA
   Director: Milos Forman
   Cast: Jack Nicholson, Louise Fletcher, Brad Dourif
   Screenplay. Bo Goldman and Lawrence Hauben
   Based on the book by Ken Kesey

3. **DEAD POETS SOCIETY**
   1989, USA
   Director: Peter Weir
   Cast: Robin Williams, Robert Sean Leonard, Ethan Hawke
   Screenplay: Tom Schulman

4. **BLADE RUNNER**
   1982, USA
   Director: Ridley Scott
   Cast: Harrison Ford, Rutger Hauer, Sean Young
   Screenplay: Hampton Fancher, David Webb Peoples, Roland Kibbee
   Based on the book by Philip K. Dick

5. **THE BRIDGES OF MADISON COUNTY**
   1995, USA
   Director: Clint Eastwood
   Cast: Clint Eastwood, Meryl Streep, Annie Corley
   Screenplay: Richard LaGravenese
   Based on the book avRobert James Waller

6. **WHEN WE WERE KINGS**
   1996, USA
   Director: Leon Gast
   Cast: Muhammad Ali, George Forman, Don King

1. -Might as well call it white jack!

2. -That's funny. That plane's dustin' crops where there ain't no crops.

3. -Top o' the world, Ma....Top o' the world.

4. -When a man says "no" to Champagne, he says "no" to life.

5. -Well, I'm sure I'd feel much worse if I weren't under such heavy sedation.

6. -Toto, I've got a feeling we're not in Kansas anymore.

ANSWERS >

1.   OCEAN'S ELEVEN
       1960, USA
       Director: Lewis Milestone
       Cast: Frank Sinatra, Dean Martin, Sammy Davis Jr
       Screenplay: George Clayton Johnson, Jack Golden Russell, Harry
       Brown, Charles Lederer and Billy Wilder

2.   NORTH BY NORTHWEST
       1959, USA
       Director: Alfred Hitchcock
       Cast: Cary Grant, Eva Marie Saint, James Mason
       Screenplay: Ernest Lehman

3.   WHITE HEAT
       1949, USA
       Director: Raoul Walsh
       Cast: James Cagney, Virginia Mayo, Edmond O'Brien
       Screenplay: Virginia Kellogg, Ivan Goff and Ben Roberts

4.   THE DEER HUNTER
       1978, USA
       Director: Michael Cimino
       Cast: Robert De Niro, Christopher Walken, Meryl Streep
       Screenplay: Michael Cimino, Louis Garfinkle, Quinn K. Redeker and
       Deric Washburn

5.   THIS IS SPINAL TAP
       1984, USA
       Director: Rob Reiner
       Cast: Michael McKean, Christopher Guest, Harry Shearer
       Screenplay: Christopher Guest, Michael McKean, Rob Reiner and
       Harry Shearer

6.   THE WIZARD OF OZ
       1939, USA
       Director: Victor Fleming
       Cast: Judy Garland, Ray Bolger, Bert Lahr
       Screenplay: Noel Langley, Florence Ryerson and Edgar Allan Woolf
       Based on the book by L. Frank Baum

1. -There's nothing more life-affirming than getting the shit kicked outta ya.

2. -I'm a spoke on a wheel. I am... and so are you.

3. -Twenty dwarves took turns doing handstands on the carpet.

4. -Sweetheart, you can't buy the necessities of life with cookies.

5. -They asked me if I'd seen any strangers in the neighborhood.

6. -You get what you settle for.

ANSWERS >

1.   DRUGSTORE COWBOY
     1989, USA
     Director: Gus Van Sant
     Cast: Matt Dillon, Kelly Lynch, James Remar
     Screenplay: Gus Van Sant, Daniel Yost and William S. Burroughs
     Based on the book by James Fogle

2.   DONNIE BRASCO
     1997, USA
     Director: Mike Newell
     Cast: Al Pacino, Johnny Depp, Michael Madsen
     Screenplay: Paul Attanasio
     Based on the book by Joseph D. Pistone and Richard Woodley

3.   BUGSY
     1991, USA
     Director: Barry Levinson
     Cast: Warren Beatty, Annette Bening, Harvey Keitel
     Screenplay: James Toback. Based on the book by Dean Jennings

4.   EDWARD SCISSORHANDS
     1990, USA
     Director: Tim Burton
     Cast: Johnny Depp, Winona Ryder, Dianne West
     Screenplay: Tim Burton and Caroline Thompson

5.   CLOSE ENCOUNTERS OF THE THIRD KIND
     1977, USA
     Director: Steven Spielberg
     Cast: Richard Dreyfuss, Francois Truffaut, Teri Garr
     Screenplay: Steven Spielberg, Hal Barwood, Jerry Belson, John Hill
     and Matthew Robbins

6.   THELMA & LOUISE
     1991, USA
     Director: Ridley Scott
     Cast: Susan Sarandon, Geena Davis, Harvey Keitel
     Screenplay: Callie Khouri

1.   -Nothing more foolish than a man chasin' his hat.

2.   -God made men. Men made slaves.

   Ten Commandment

3.   -This whole world's wild at heart and weird on top.

4.   -I'll never look like Barbie. Barbie doesn't have bruises.

5.   The only thing I'll ever lay is a rug!

6.   -The Force can have a strong influence on a weak mind.

   A New Hope

1.   MILLER'S CROSSING
     1990, USA
     Director: Joel Coen
     Cast: Gabriel Byrne, Albert Finney, Marcia Gay Harden
     Screenplay: Joel Coen and Ethan Coen
     Based on the book by Dashiell Hammett

2.   THE TEN COMMANDMENTS
     1956, USA
     Director: Cecil B Demille
     Cast: Charlton Heston, Yul Brynner, Anne Baxter
     Screenplay: J.H. Ingraham, A.E. Southon, Dorothy Clarke Wilson,
     Æneas MacKenzie, Jesse Lasky Jr., Jack Gariss and
     Fredric M. Frank

3.   WILD AT HEART
     1990, USA
     Director: David Lynch
     Cast: Nicolas Cage, Laura Dern, Diane Ladd
     Screenplay: David Lynch
     Based on the book by Barry Gifford

4.   SID & NANCY
     1986, USA
     Director: Alex Cox
     Cast: Gary Oldman, Chloe Webb, Drew Schofield
     Screenplay: Alex Cox and Abbe Wool

5.   ROCK 'N' ROLL HIGH SCHOOL
     1979, USA
     Director: Allan Arkush, Joe Dante
     Cast: P.J Soles, Vincent van Patten, Clint Howard
     Screenplay: Richard Whitley, Russ Dronch

6.   STAR WARS
     1977, USA
     Director: George Lucas
     Cast: Mark Hamill, Harrison Ford, Carrie Fisher
     Screenplay: George Lucas

1.   -The best goodbyes are short. Adieu.

2.   -I'm too old for this shit!

3.   -In case I forget to tell you later - I had a really good time tonight.

4.   -I swear to GOD, George, if you ever EXISTED I'd divorce you.

5.   -Just like a Wop to bring a knife to a gunfight.

6.   -In Rome, dignity shortens life even more surely than disease.

ANSWERS >

1.   THE MALTESE FALCON
     1941, USA
     Director: John Huston
     Cast: Humphrey Bogart, Mary Astor, Peter Lorre
     Screenplay: John Huston
     Based on the book by Dashell Hammett

2.   LETHAL WEAPON
     1987, USA
     Director: Richard Donner
     Cast: Mel Gibson, Danny Glover, Gary Busey
     Screenplay: Shane Black

3.   PRETTY WOMAN
     1990, USA
     Director: Garry Marshall
     Cast: Richard Gere, Julia Roberts, Ralph Bellamy
     Screenplay: J.F Lawton

4.   WHO'S AFRAID OF VIRGINIA WOOLF?
     1966, USA
     Director: Mike Nichols
     Cast: Elizabeth Taylor, Richard Burton, George Segal
     Screenplay: Edward Albee and Ernest Lehman

5.   THE UNTOUCHABLES
     1987, USA
     Director: Brian De Palma
     Cast: Kevin Costner, Sean Connery, Charles Martin Smith
     Screenplay: David Mamet
     Based on the book by Oscar Fraley and Eliot Ness and Paul Robsky

6.   SPARTACUS
     1960, USA
     Director: Stanley Kubrick
     Cast: Kirk Douglas, Laurence Olivier, Jean Simmons
     Screenplay: Dalton Trumbo, Calder Willingham and Peter Ustinov
     Based on the book by Howard Fast

1. -We seem to be made to suffer. It's our lot in life.

2. -Pain can be controlled; you just disconnect it.

3. I'm just a mean green mother from outer space and I'm bad!

4. -Uh, well, sir... I ain't a real cowboy. But I am one helluva stud!

5. -You are the Duke of New York! You're A Number 1!

6. -I heard someone screaming, and it was me.

ANSWERS >

1. **STAR WARS**
    1977, USA
    Director: George Lucas
    Cast: Mark Hamill, Harrison Ford, Carrie Fisher
    Screenplay: George Lucas

2. **THE TERMINATOR**
    1984, USA
    Director: James Cameron
    Cast: Arnold Schwartzenegger, Michael Biehn,
    Linda Hamilton Screenplay: James Cameron, Gale Anne Hurd,
    William Wisher Jr and Harlan Ellison

3. **LITTLE SHOP OF HORRORS**
    1986, USA
    Director: Frank Oz
    Cast: Rick Moranis, Ellen Greene, Vincent Gardenia
    Screenplay: Charles B. Griffith and Howard Ashman

4. **MIDNIGHT COWBOY**
    1969, USA
    Director: John Schlesinger
    Cast: Dustin Hoffman, Jon Voight, Sylvia Miles
    Screenplay: Waldo Salt
    Based on the book by James Leo Herlihy

5. **ESCAPE FROM NEW YORK**
    1981, USA
    Director: John Carpenter
    Cast: Kurt Russell, Lee Van Cleef, Ernest Borgnine
    Screenplay: John Carpenter and Nick Castle

6. **THE ACCUSED**
    1988, USA
    Director: Jonathan Kaplan
    Cast: Kelly McGillis, Jodie Foster, Bernie Coulson
    Screenplay: Tom Topor

1. -He knew the risks. He didn't have to be there.
    It rains, you get wet.

2. -You know what the Queen said? "If I had balls, I'd be King".

3. -Some places are like people: some shine and some don't.

4. -When they come...they come at what you love.

5. -Wax on, wax off...

6. -Divine decadence darling!

ANSWERS >

1.   **HEAT**
        1995, USA
        Director: Michael Mann
        Cast: Al Pacino, Robert De Niro, Val Kilmer
        Screenplay: Michael Mann

2.   **MEAN STREETS**
        1973, USA
        Director: Martin Scorsese
        Cast: Robert De Niro, Harvey Keitel, David Proval
        Screenplay: Martin Scorsese and Mardik Martin

3.   **THE SHINING**
        1980, USA
        Director: Stanley Kubrick
        Cast: Jack Nicholson, Shelley Duvall, Danny Lloyd
        Screenplay: Stanley Kubrick and Diane Johnson
        Based on the book by Stephen King

4.   **THE GODFATHER PART III**
        1990, USA
        Director: Francis Ford Coppola
        Cast: Al Pacino, Diane Keaton, Talia Shire
        Screenplay: Mario Puzo and Francis Ford Coppola

5.   **THE KARATE KID**
        1984, USA
        Director: John G Avildsen
        Cast: Ralph Macchio, Noriyuki Morita, Elisabeth Shue
        Screenplay: Robert Mark Kamen

6.   **CABARET**
        1972, USA
        Director: Bob Fosse
        Cast: Liza Minelli, Michael York, Helmut Griem
        Screenplay: John Van Druten, Joe Masteroff, Jay Presson Allen and
        Hugh Wheeler
        Based on the book by Christopher Isherwood

1. -Play it cool, boy. Real cool.

    West Side Story

2. -Get busy living, or get busy dying. That's goddamn right.

3. -What'd the old man trade for those guys? A used puck bag?

4. -You're tearing me apart!

5. -It ain't like it used to be, but it'll do.

6. -They laughed at me, Mama.

ANSWERS >

1.   **WEST SIDE STORY**
    1961, USA
    Director: Robert Wise, Jerome Robbins
    Cast: Natalie Wood, Richard Beymer, George Chakiris
    Screenplay: Jerome Robbins, Arthur Laurents and Ernest Lehman
    Based on Romeo and Julia by William Shakespeare

2.   **THE SHAWSHANK REDEMPTION**
    1994, USA
    Director: Frank Darabont
    Cast: Tim Robbins, Morgan Freeman, Bob Gunton
    Screenplay: Frank Darabont
    Based on the book by Stephen King

3.   **SLAP SHOT**
    1977, USA
    Director: George Roy
    Cast: Paul Newman, Michael Ontkean, Lindsay Crouse
    Screenplay: Nancy Dowd

4.   **REBEL WITHOUT A CAUSE**
    1955, USA
    Director: Nicholas Ray
    Cast: James Dean, Natalie Wood, Sal Mineo
    Screenplay: Nicholas Ray, Irving Shulman and Stewart Stern

5.   **THE WILD BUNCH**
    1969, USA
    Director: Sam Peckinpah
    Cast: William Holden, Ernest Borgnine, Robert Ryan
    Screenplay: Walon Green, Roy N. Sickner, Walon Green and
    Sam Peckinpah

6.   **CARRIE**
    1976, USA
    Director: Brian De Palma
    Cast: Sissy Spacek, Piper Laurie, William Katt
    Screenplay: Lawrence D. Cohen
    Based on the book by Stephen King

1. -Cyborgs don't feel pain. I do. Don't do that again.

    The Terminator

2. -To be on the wire is life. The rest is waiting.

3. -I would like, if I may, to take you on a strange journey.

4. -Have you had a close encounter?

5. -Now take that underwear off your head. Enough's enough.

6. -Rockin' good news.

ANSWERS >

1.   THE TERMINATOR
       1984, USA
       Director: James Cameron
       Cast: Arnold Schwartzenegger, Michael Biehn,
       Linda Hamilton
       Screenplay: James Cameron, Gale Anne Hurd, William Wisher Jr and
       Harlan Ellison

2.   ALL THAT JAZZ
       1979, USA
       Director: Bob Fosse
       Cast: Roy Schneider, Jessica Lange, Ann Reinking
       Screenplay: Robert Alan Aurthur and Bob Fosse

3.   THE ROCKY HORROR PICTURE SHOW
       1975, USA
       Director: Jim Sharman
       Cast: Tim Curry, Susan Sarandon, Barry Bostwick
       Screenplay: Richard O'Brien, Jim Sharman

4.   CLOSE ENCOUNTERS OF THE THIRD KIND
       1977, USA
       Director: Steven Spielberg
       Cast: Richard Dreyfuss, Francois Truffaut, Teri Garr
       Screenplay: Steven Spielberg, Hal Barwood, Jerry Belson, John Hill
       and Matthew Robbins

5.   KELLY'S HEROES
       1970, USA
       Director: Brian G Hutton
       Cast: Clint Eastwood, Telly Savalas, Don Rickles
       Screenplay: Troy Kennedy-Martin

6.   WILD AT HEART
       1990, USA
       Director: David Lynch
       Cast: Nicolas Cage, Laura Dern, Diane Ladd
       Screenplay: David Lynch
       Based on the book by Barry Gifford

Index

Index

Index

Index

Index

X

CONFESSIONS
Shameful Secrets of Everyday People
91-974396-6-5
Humor

Eavesdropping in the Confessional

Like being a fly on the wall in any church confessional, these incredible real online admissions of people's darkest secrets are alternately disturbing, whimsical and hilarious. Sure to spark interesting conversations, this is the perfect therapeutic gift to share with friends and loved ones (and perhaps detested enemies, with certain confessions circled in red and "I know your secret" handwritten nearby).

Dirty MovieQuoteBook
91-974396-9-X
Humor/Film

Saucy Sayings of Cinema

With over 700 saucy, sexy quotes from the funniest and most sordid films ever produced. A movie quiz game in a book. An excellent source of fresh pick-up or put-down lines, this titillating guide is sure to put anyone in the mood for love.

BLA BLA - 600 Incredibly Useless Facts
Something to Talk About When You Have Nothing else to Say
91-974882-1-6
Humor

A Know-It-All's Handbook

Everyone needs something to blurt out during uncomfortable silences and
ice-breaker moments. This fascinating handbook of hilarious, arcane and
bizarre tidbits will make its bearer a hit at party conversation and trivia contests.

The World's Coolest Baby Names
91-974883-1-3
Pop Culture

A Name Book for the 21st Century Parent

A perfect name guide to spice up any baby shower name game.
Baby names aren't handed down anymore, and the coolest names are as
much from pop culture as from the Bible. Hybrid names from popular and
arcane sources in literature, television, and film create some very memorable
name combinations. Includes the amusing trivia behind the names' origins
and is sure to spark scads of arguments in expectant families everywhere!

Gordon Gecko - Wallstreet - Kissy Suzuki - you only live twice -
Bobby Peru - wild at heart - Holly Golightly - breakfast at tiffany's -
Alexander de Large - a clock work orange - Phoebe Buffay - friends

The Pet Cookbook
Have your best friend for dinner
91-974883-4-8
Humor/Cooking

Domesticated Delicacies from Around the World

On a global scale, one man's pet is another man's supper, and this wild
cookbook shares the best recipes from around the world on how to
prepare those delectable little dishes from the domesticated animal kingdom
Scorpion Soup with a Sting, Pony 'n' Pepperoni Pizza, Parrot Piroge, and
Goldfish Tortilla Wrap are just a few samples of the eclectic world cuisine
within. Decidedly not for vegetarians.

*No animals were hurt during the making of this book.

SCORPION SOUP WITH A STING
CREAMY PARAKEET PASTA
PARROT PIROGE
GUINEA PIG PIE
GOLDFISH TORTILLA WRAP
MUD TURTLE RISOTTO